Collectors' Bank Notes
Treasury and Bank of England

By Pam West & Chris Henry Perkins
15th Edition © 2008

INTERNATIONAL STANDARD BOOK No:
978-0-948964-72-5

A fully updated compilation of averaged selling prices drawn from dealers' lists, auctions, notaphily magazines and websites.

The preceding 2006 15th edition of this book was
ISBN 0-948964-58-8.

Errors and Omissions:

Every effort has been made to ensure that the information and price data contained within this book is accurate and complete. However, errors do sometimes have a habit of creeping in unnoticed, and with this in mind the following email address has been established for notifications of omissions and errors: info@rotographic.com. Readers within the UK can also call the telephone number below.

www.rotographic.com
0871 871 5122

In Association with

Contents

Introduction

Welcome to the 15th edition of Collectors' Banknotes. This is the first colour edition, and the images have been reproduced at the highest possible resolution.

I admit to being primarily a coin dealer with limited involvement with banknotes, and the whole task of producing a banknote price guide was incredibly daunting at first. The last edition sold well but for this new edition, to ensure everything was as accurate as possible, I have called upon the help of Pam West, who is one of the countries leading banknote experts. Pam has been kind enough to update all the prices and to donate a few images of scarcer notes.

Pam has corrected a few minor errors, and has also added data - mainly concerning note serial number ranges - in order to make this book accurate according to current information and research. The market over the last couple of years has been strong and many notes are priced much higher in this new edition than they were in the last.

Pam and I both hope that this book provides you with accurate and complete information!

Chris Henry Perkins and Pam West
www.predecimal.com / www.britishnotes.com
December 2007

The Layout of this catalogue

As in previous editions, the Treasury notes are dealt with first in spite of the fact that the Bank of England issued notes appeared some two hundred years earlier. Treasury notes were issued for a specific length of time, and because they have an exact start and end point, they are complete. Bank of England notes are still being produced and it is logical therefore to have them after the Treasury notes so that they can be added to as new notes are issued.

Collectors' Banknotes 2008 is therefore laid out in three sections:

The first section covers Treasury Notes printed between 1914 - 1927 including the unofficial Shilling, Half Crown and Five Shillings notes and the Dardanelles campaign overprint notes.

The second section covers Bank of England Notes 1694 - 1928, and includes approximate values for the earlier very rare banknotes where information is available.

The third section covers the modern Bank of England issues, from 1928 - date. This section is naturally fully updated with the new banknote issues each year.

The Layout of the Listings

The listings throughout the book are arranged in six or seven columns. The first column is always the reference number, this number is unique to this book and would have remained unchanged since the first edition (unless stated). New issues are given new reference numbers. The second column is for the date of the Note and the third column will contain the name of the signatory and other relevant variety information. Columns four to seven contain the values of the notes in varying states of preservation (see the introduction to grading on page 4).

Serial Prefix Combinations

At the beginning of most bank note ranges, the serial prefix format is specified along the following guidelines:

LNN = Letter-Number-Number e.g A12
NNL = Number-Number-Letter e.g 12A
LLNN = Letter-Letter-Number-Number e.g AB12
LNNL = Letter-Number-Number-Letter e.g A12B

L/N = Letter over Number e.g $\frac{A}{1}$

L2/N = Letter and small indicated Number over another Number e.g $\frac{L2}{1}$

Other combinations, should they occur will hopefully be quite obvious.

Some note types have either a dot or a dash under the 'No'. Something like: N $\overset{\circ}{\cdot}$ or N $\overset{\circ}{\_}$

A RADAR number reads the same backwards as it does fowards, e.g 796697.

An Introduction to Bank Note Grading

Grading of Banknotes often comes down to a matter of personal opinion and the ability to grade notes to a degree of accuracy often takes years of experience with different banknote types. Just as with coins, the most common way of grading banknotes is to assign a grade from a range of: Poor, Fair, Fine, Very Fine, Extremely Fine and Uncirculated. Notes that fall between the 'whole' grades are often referred to as 'GVF' (Good Very Fine), 'NEF' (Near Extremely Fine), or even 'AEF' (About Extremely Fine). Only perfect notes in as new condition should be labelled 'Uncirculated'.

For novice collectors a penalty point system has been devised to help with grading. Please note that not all aspects of banknote condition are covered and often the best way to learn how to grade with any degree of accuracy is to befriend an experienced collector or dealer.

Assuming a perfect note is 100%, start at 100 and deduct points based on the following:

Holes	Each pin hole	5 Points
	Larger holes	10+ Points
Edges	Fluffed or uncrisp portions	5 Points
	Tears short of design	10 Points
	Tears reaching into design	20 Points
Folds	Very minor 'Cashiers bend'	2 Points
	Discernable but unsharp fold	5 Points
	Sharp, distinct crease	10 Points
	Several folds (squeezed into small pocket)	20 Points
Dirt/Wear	Area of just noticable discolouration	5 Points
	Grubbiness - Cashiers marks	10 Points
	Partial illegibility from dirt or wear	20 Points

For anything else that makes you less than happy and has not been penalised above deduct: 1 - 5 Points

Range: Up to 15% Poor. 16 - 30% Fair. 31 - 60% Around Fine. Very Fine 75 - 90%. Extremely Fine around 90 - 97% and About Uncirculated (AUNC) between 98 - 99%.

SECTION 1

Treasury Notes 1914 to 1928

The Chancellor of the day, Lloyd George, just a few hours after the midnight Declaration of War, touched on the need to preserve the country's gold. The issue of notes for one pound and for ten shillings were to circulate 'As full as sovereigns and half-sovereigns are current and shall be legal tender in the United Kingdom for the payment of any amount"

The Bank of England felt that large numbers of low-value notes wouldn't be "safe" unless they were printed on special, handmade paper. This meant a relatively slow output. The Chancellor wanted them immediately, so instead, they were produced by the treasury. His announcement in Parliament was on August 5th; Waterlow Brothers and Layton provided the first of the new one pound notes on August 7th! Obviously, there must have been earlier discussions and preparations for such a speedy result. Possibly, a very fine Crystal Ball revealed the inevitability of The Great War.

An astonishing achievement, carried out over a single weekend, saw the printing of a vast number of the new notes. They were printed on ungummed postage stamp paper and carried the G.R. cypher watermark. Bearing the signature of the SECRETARY TO THE TREASURY John Bradbury, the pound notes were printed in black and, appearing just one week later, the ten shilling notes were in red. Both notes were the same size and were printed on only one side of the paper. It was advisable to have all your notes face upwards before counting. Many found face down, it is said, were thrown away as scrap paper! Thomas De La Rue and Company assisted Waterlow Brothers and Layton to produce the ten shilling note. Almost at once, a second series was devised. This time banknote paper was used and a much more elaborate watermark incorporated: the Royal Cypher, value, rose, thistle, shamrock, and daffodil. Still on one side only and in the same colours, some sorting assistance was provided by varying the sizes slightly between the two values. Included in this second series is the issue of: THE DARDANELLES CAMPAIGN Overprints (pages 9 and 13). Third issue "Bradburys", chiefly in brown (£1) and green (10/-) speedily followed, Both sides were printed and the "typical" British banknote was established.

The original purpose of the Treasury note was to gather in the gold. So successful was the exercise that silver was targeted and notes were prepared for five shillings (5/-), half-a-crown (2/6d), and even one shilling (1/-). Fear of runaway inflation through notes unbacked by real assets led to the destruction of most of these.

Two Shillings and Sixpence
Image used with permission of Pam West Britishnotes.

H.M. TREASURY NOTES
(These three fractions not officially issued)

No.	Date	Signature	Fine	VF	EF

ONE SHILLING
Central vignette of H. M. King George V. Green, brown, white 104x66mm - 4 $\frac{1}{8}$ x 2 $\frac{5}{8}$ in

RT1   1918 (Nov)   **John Bradbury:**
A/1 (probably A/1 No. 000000 only)
£5000

RT2   1919 (Nov)   **N. F. Warren fisher:**
L/N   B/- (only)   £5000

HALFCROWN
(Two Shillings and Six Pence)
Central vignette of H. M. King George V. OIive-green, chocolate and white.

RT3   1918 (Nov)   **John Bradbury:**
L/N   A/1 No. 000000   £5000
(Auction '96)   Five Colour Trial   £24,000

RT4   1919 (Nov)   **N. F. Warren-Fisher:**
L/N   A/-   £5500

FIVE SHILLINGS
Central vignette of H. M. King George V. Violet, green and white 5 x 3in -127x76mm

RT5   1917 (Dec)   **John Bradbury:**
L/N   A/-   (one known, noted 1992)   £13,300 (UNC)

RT6   1919 (Nov)   **N. F. Warren-Fisher:**
L/N   B/-   £5000

RT6
Image courtesy of
Pam West Britishnotes.

RT8a
Image courtesy of
Pam West Britishnotes.

H.M. TREASURY NOTES

No.	Date	Signature	Fine	VF	EF	UNC

TEN SHILLINGS (Type illustrated on previous page)
Small vignette at left - Very large value at right (see picture on previous page)
Red and white - Printed one side only, on stamp paper - 127 x 63.5mm - 5 x 2 $^1/_2$ in

	1914 (Aug)	**John Bradbury:**				
RT7		L/N - N$^{\circ}$ 6 digits (N$^{\circ}$ with dot under)				
		S/-		£550	£950	£1450
RT8		L/N - N$^{\circ}$ 6 digits (N$^{\circ}$ with dash under)				
		A/1	£200	£375	£900	£1200
		A/-	£150	£325	£700	£1000
RT8a		Variety has no space between prefix and serial (as on page 6)				
		A/-			£700	
RT9		L/N - N$^{\circ}$ 5 digits (A, B, C possibly other letters, N$^{\circ}$ with dot under)				
		B/-	£300	£750	£1250	

TEN SHILLINGS
UNITED KINGDOM OF GREAT BRITAIN AND IRELAND
Red and white, printed only on one side - 136 x 76mm -5 $^3/_8$ x 3 in
Watermark of wavy lines, Royal Cypher and British Emblems.

	1915	**John Bradbury:**				
RT10		L/N 5 digits - A to M				
			£100	£250	£450	£800
RT11		L1/N 5 digits - A1 to M1				
			£70	£150	£450	£850

RT10

RT11

H.M. TREASURY NOTES

No.	Date	Signature	Fine	VF	EF	UNC

TEN SHILLINGS
UNITED KINGDOM OF GREAT BRITAIN AND IRELAND
Red and white - Printed only on one side - 136 x 76mm - $5\,^3/_8$ x 3 in
Watermark of wavy lines, Royal Cypher and British Emblems

	1915	**John Bradbury:**				
RT12		L2/N A2, B2 or C2 + 5 digits				
			£150	£350	£600	£900
RT13		L/N plus 6 digits (N to Z)				
			£150	£250	£600	£900
RT14		L1/N plus 6 digits (O1 to Y1)				
			£150	£250	£600	£900
	(noted 1999)	S1/62 hand-signed by Versailles Treaty signatorys "torn" £880				
	(noted 2000)	Rounded Shamrock watermark: VF £500 (see RT23b)				

RT13
Image donated

RT14

H.M. TREASURY NOTES
"260 Days"

Under General Sir Ian Hamilton, a force of 30,000 men set sail from Lemnos with the intention of making a landing on the Peninsula of Gallipoli. First ashore, 25th April 1915, were the combined contingents from Australia and New Zealand: the ANZACS. The place of their landing has since been known as Anzac Cove. Getting ashore was relatively easy, but holding the cove in the face of brave and very tough Turkish soldiers, led by Mustafa Kemal (later called Ataturk)
brought out the best in the Anzacs who achieved, probably, the only success in a disastrous campaign.

At the tip of the peninsula was Cape Helles. Cape HELL suffices to pinpoint slaughter on a vast scale. Hour after hour the British infantry scrambled down the gang-planks leading from doors cut in the side of the "River Clyde". Most were killed before they even touched the shore. Red ripples washed on to "V" beach. At "W" beach, the 1st Lancashire Fusiliers won their historic "six Victoria Crosses before breakfast" and established a toe-hold at the cost of half their number.

Fierce counter attacks by the Turks eventually reduced all Allied positions to little more than the space they physically occupied. The great Dardanelles Expedition: which was intended to relieve the static, murderous trench warfare of France, itself became the very worst kind of trench warfare where the opposing sides were so close together that hand grenades were tossed from one to the other, and often back again before exploding. The Turks, by digging their trenches so close to their enemy, avoided being shelled by the British fleet. Attacks by the Allies couldn't push back the Turks; massive counter attacks, with huge casualties, couldn't dislodge the Allies, Gallipoli was a disaster.

On the morning of 20th December, the Turks, at first with nervous suspicion, were astonished to find that the entire Anzac force had gone. On the 9th January, the British forces at Cape Helles also "disappeared" in the same way: stealthily, during the night. Both "withdrawals" were brilliantly carried out without casualties.

TEN SHILLINGS - DARDANELLES CAMPAIGN OVERPRINT
Arabic writing in black over RT13)

No.	Signature	Fine	VF	EF	UNC
RT15	**John Bradbury:** L/N plus 6 digits Y/N and Z/N	£500	£700	£1500	

Convincing overprint forgeries (on genuine notes) have been seen bearing other than Y or Z serial numbers.

RT15

H.M. TREASURY NOTES

No.	Date	Signature	Fine	VF	EF	UNC

TEN SHILLINGS

Green, purple, brown and white - 138 x 78mm - 5 $^1/_2$ x 3 $^1/_8$ in
Watermark: Royal Cypher - TEN SHILLINGS - four emblems

No.	Date	Signature	Fine	VF	EF	UNC
	1918 (Oct)	**John Bradbury:**				
RT16		L/N № (black with dot under №)				
		A/N		£350	£600	£1000
RT17		L/N № (black with dash under №)				
		A/N	£150	£450	£750	£1000
RT18		L/N № (red with dot under №)				
		B/N, C/N	£480	£900	£1600	
RT19		L/N № (red with dash under №)				
		B/N, C/N	£140	£250	£500	£950
	1919 (Sep)	**N.F. Warren-Fisher:**				
RT20		L/N № (red with dot under №)				
		D/N	£80	£180	£350	£600
		E/N, F/N, G/N	£50	£160	£320	£550
		H/N	£80	£180	£350	£600

RT19

RT20

RT22

H.M. TREASURY NOTES

No.	Date	Signature	Fine	VF	EF	UNC

TEN SHILLINGS

Green, purple, brown and white - 138 x 78mm - 5 $^1/_2$ x 3 $^1/_8$ in
Watermark: Royal Cypher - TEN SHILLINGS - four emblems

N.F. Warren-Fisher (continued):

			Fine	VF	EF	UNC
RT21		L/N N$^o_{\_}$ (red with dash under N°)				
		D/N	£60	£180	£350	£550
		E/N, F/N, G/N	£40	£160	£340	£500
		H/N	£60	£180	£350	£550
RT22		L/N (" N° " omitted. J/- to S/-)				
		J/N and K/N	£50	£140	£250	£450
		L/N to R/N	£50	£140	£250	
		S/N	£50	£140	£250	
	1927 (July)	Now reads "UNITED KINGDOM OF GREAT BRITAIN AND NORTHERN IRELAND"				
RT23a		L/N (as RT22)				
		S/N to W/N	£60	£130	£260	£450
RT23b		The watermark has a mis-shaped shamrock. See below				
		L/12, 32, 52, 72 and 92	£450	£900		

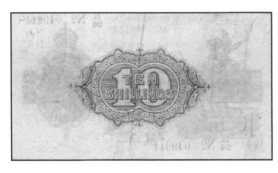

Reverse type common to RT16 - RT23b

RT23b - Watermark: The right shamrock leaf is rounded, not heart shaped, and does not match the other leaves.

H.M. TREASURY NOTES

No.	Date	Signature	Fine	VF	EF	UNC

ONE POUND

Watermark: Royal Cypher, "POSTAGE" - Small vignette at left - very large value at right. Black and White - Printed on one side using postage stamp paper - 127 x 63mm - 5 x 2 $^1/_2$ in

1914 (Aug) **John Bradbury:**

No.	Signature	Fine	VF	EF	UNC
RT25a.	Capital A. (with stop)	£700	£1100	£2200	
RT25b.	Capital B. (with stop)	£650	£100	£2100	
RT25c.	Capital C. (with stop)	£700	£1100	£2200	
RT26a	Capital A (no stop)	£1000	£1700	£3600	
RT26b	Capital B (no stop)	£900	£1600	£3500	
RT26c	Capital C (no stop)	£100	£1700	£3600	
RT27a	L/N N⁰ (with dot under N⁰) 4 digits	£1200	£2700		
RT27b	L/N N⁰ (with dot under N⁰) 5 digits	£900	£1600	£3500	
RT27c	L/N N⁰ (with dot under N⁰) 6 digits	£600	£950	£1600	

Similar to RT27c   A Trial "W/87 000000" at auction (1994) £1980

	Colour trial w/mk stars/circles (1998)				£1100
RT27d	L/N N⁰ (with dot under N⁰) 7 digits	£1000	£2400		
RT28a	L/N N⁰ (with dash under N⁰) 4 digits	£1400	£2900		
RT28b	L/N N⁰ (with dash under N⁰) 5 digits	£750	£1500		

RT29a	L/N N⁰ (with dash under N⁰) 6 small 3mm digits				
		£500	£900	£1500	
RT29b	L/N N⁰ (with dot under N⁰) 7 small digits				
		£800	£1300	£2500	
RT29c	L/N N⁰ (with dash under N⁰) 6 small 4mm digits				
		£650	£900	£1800	

| RT30 | LL/N - 6 digits. AA/- | | | £3000 | |
| | BB/- to LL/- (no II/-) | £400 | £750 | £1400 | |

| RT31 | LL/N - No. 4 digits (Stop after "No", not under it) Rare | | | | |
| | | £1250+ | £3000+ | | |

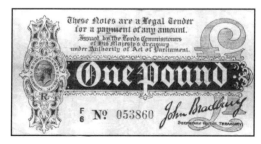

RT27c
Image donated

H.M. TREASURY NOTES

No.	Date	Signature	Fine	VF	EF	UNC

ONE POUND

Watermark: Wavy lines, Royal cypher, ONE POUND and four emblems.
Black and White - Printed on one side using bank note paper - 149 x 85mm - 5 $^7/_8$ x 3 $^1/_4$ in

	1914 (Oct)	**John Bradbury:**				
		(Spink 1998) Trial sheet, undated, black and white two notes "small tear". hammer price: £1,100				
RT32		L/N plus five digits (A, with gaps, to Z)				
			£250	£500	£850	
RT33		L1/N plus five digits (A1, with gaps, to L1)				
			£120	£250	£500	£800

RT32

ONE POUND - DARDANELLES CAMPAIGN OVERPRINT
(see page 9 for 10/- note and more details)
Arabic writing in red over RT32

RT34		**John Bradbury:**				
		F, J, M, P, K, Y	£3000	£5000	£9000	

Notes bearing prefixes other than F, J, M, P, K or Y might be genuine notes with fraudulent overprints. Expert advice should be sought.

RT34
Image courtesy of
R J Marles

H.M. TREASURY NOTES

No.	Date	Signature	Fine	VF	EF	UNC

ONE POUND
Watermark: Diagonal lines in alternate bands, ONE POUND and emblems etc.
Brown, purple, green on white or cream paper - St. George and dragon to left
- 152 x 85mm - 6 x 3 $^3/_8$ in
UNITED KINGDOM OF GREAT BRITAIN AND IRELAND

No.	Date	Signature	Fine	VF	EF	UNC
RT35	1917 (Jan)	**John Bradbury**:				
		L/N (A to H and Z)				
		A/1		£120	£250	£400
		A/-		£70	£180	£280
		B/- to H/-	£20	£70	£180	£280
		Z/-	£40	£160	£280	£480
RT36	1919 (Sep)	**N. F. Warren-Fisher**:				
		L/N (K to Z, without Q and V)				
		K/-		£75	£160	£280
		L/- to Y/-		£65	£130	£250
		Z/-		£85	£180	£300
RT36a		L/N with a much broader 'Nº' and a bolder dot. See image below.				
	(Noted)	R/70		£90		

RT36a

RT36, serial with thinner Nº

RT36a, serial with broad Nº and large dot

No.	Date	Signature	Fine	VF	EF	UNC
RT37	1919 (Sep)	**N. F. Warren-Fisher**: Central watermark				
		L1/N Nº (A1 to R1, without I or Q, round dot under Nº)				
		A1/-	£80	£170	£250	
		B1/- to•R1/-	£65	£140	£220	
		Z1/-	£75	£170	£280	
RTS37		A1/13 Overprinted 'SPECIMEN' at bottom left and top right -				
RT38		II1 to R1 except L1	£180	£330	£450	
		L1/N Nº (with square dot)	£220	£400	£600	
		Z1/-	£220	£400	£600	

H.M. TREASURY NOTES

No.	Date	Signature	Fine	VF	EF	UNC

ONE POUND

Details as previous, but now reads:
UNITED KINGDOM OF GREAT BRITAIN AND <u>NORTHERN</u> IRELAND

	1927 (July)	**N. F. Warren-Fisher:**				
RT39		L1/N N^o (S to Z without V and Y, round dot under N^o)				
		S1/-	£30	£80	£170	£300
		T1/- to X1/-	£25	£70	£160	£260
		Z1/-	£40	£90	£190	£330
RT40		L1/N N^o (serials as RT39, square dot under N^o)				
		S1/- to Z1/-	£80	£220	£340	£600

RT39

Below: The reverse common to RT35 - RT40

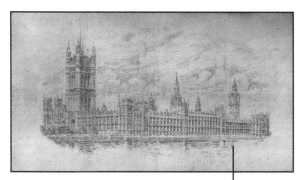

Look out for, and report to Rotographic if an anchor appears here——

SECTION TWO:

BANK OF ENGLAND NOTES 1694 - 1928

There were notes even before the Bank of England came into existence in 1694. Gentlemens' agreements in writing were promises (or promissory notes) to reimburse whoever eventually presented the note:

"Thus a note from A to B promising to pay £20 for some shipment would be used by B to pay C for corn. Then A would pay C instead (of B) the original amount of money':

(From D.M. Miller's "Bank of England and Treasury Notes 1694 - 1970").

D.M. Miller also tells how notes for despatch to London were first cut in half and the two halves sent by separate stage coaches to defeat the highwayman. Provided both consignments survived the coach trip, the notes were re-joined, encashed, and cancelled; the cancellation was reinforced by punching or cutting a hole to prevent re-presentation.

The Bank was particularly upset by attempts to forge its notes. Simply being caught in possession of a forgery meant certain transportation. This was harsh when one considers that some forgers were skilled enough to fool bank cashiers. There were so many prosecutions, however, that jurors ignored even the most damning evidence because the punishment was considered too severe. The Bank later endeavoured to ease the situation by arranging for the convict's family to accompany him, and by ensuring that they had some cash upon arrival.

Knowingly possessing a forged note is still an offence. Sending a suspect note to the bank for verification will result in the issue of a Memorandum of Detention if the note proves to be counterfeit; then it will be destroyed. The Bank might well consider that forgeries of notes that are no longer legal tender offer a lesser threat, but in actual fact, Bank of England notes are actually redeemable at the bank for face value indefinitely.

By 1725 there were notes in the range £20, £30, etc, to £100, £200, £300, £400, £500 and £1,000. Notes for £10, £15 and £25 were issued between 1759 and 1765, but none for under £10. Provincial banks and even tradesmen started issuing notes for any sum: in the extreme for one penny! Notes under £5 were eventually prohibited (except in Scotland), but it was too late. Notes issued without sufficient backing assets leads to bankruptcy. Over 100 banks met this fate, and a further 300 eventually closed.

Prosperity brought about by the efforts to pursue the wars with France caused a massive revival of little banks until their number exceeded 700. When war with France was drawing to a close, all the steam went out of the economy and customers found they needed the substance (gold) rather than the promise (notes). Hundreds of banks collapsed and the situation brought even the Bank of England to its knees.

It was found that many would have survived if they could have called-up their cash reserves in time. To remove that difficulty, the Bank of England opened branches to shorten the lines of communication; Birmingham, Bristol, Exeter, Gloucester, Leeds, Liverpool and Manchester branches were followed by others at Belfast, Cardiff, Hull, Leicester, Newcastle, Norwich, Portsmouth, Southampton and Swansea.

Of the bank notes up to, and including Chief Cashier Horace George Bowen, only Henry Hase notes appear with any frequency. Due to the rarity of the 18th and 19th century notes there is insufficient trading to compile useful averages. Only actual offers, or auction results can provide a true guide to value.

BANK OF ENGLAND NOTES 1694 - 1928

Few notes are known to have survived from the period up to Charles Jewson.

The Chief Cashiers 1694 - 1777:
- John Kendrick - 1694
- Thomas Speed - 1694 to 1699
- Thomas Madockes - 1699 to 1739
- James Collier with Daniel Race - 1739 to 1751
- Daniel Race with Elias Simes - 1751 to 1759
- Daniel Race - 1759 to 1775
- Charles Jewson - 1775 to 1777

No.	Date	Signature/face value/details	Fine
		Abraham Newland - 1778 to 1807:	
REB1	1797	£1, note No.2, at auction 1993	£57,000
REB2	1798 - 1801	£1, smaller plate, printed signature	£3500
REB3	1801 - 1803	£1, new watermark, standard size	£2200
REB4	1803 - 1807	£1, value in watermark	£2000
REB5	1797	£2, hand written signature	-
REB6	1798 - 1801	£2, smaller plate, printed signature	£6000
REB7	1801 - 1803	£2, standard size	£5000
REB8	1803 - 1805	£2, value in watermark	-
REB9	1805 - 1807	£2, new design	£4000
REB10	1793	£5	£12,000
REB11	1798 - 1801	£10, smaller plate, printed signature	£20,000
REB12	1805 - 1807	£10, Bank of England heading	£20,000
REB13		£15	-
REB14		£20	-
REB15		£100, at auction 2000 (AVF)	£40,250
		Henry Hase - 1807 to 1829:	
REB31		£1, hand written date, countersigned	£4000
REB32		£1, hand written date, not countersigned	£3000
REB33		£1, printed date and serials	£1400
REB34		£1, emergency issue, dated 1821	£1400
REB35		£2, hand written date, countersigned	£4250
REB36		£2, hand written date, not countersigned	£4000
REB37		£2, printed date and serials	£3000
REB38		£5, hand written	£7000
REB39		£5, printed date and serials	£6000
REB39T		£5, Trial Hase printed in France, at auction 2000	£1200

Hase notes were also issued in £10, £15, £20, £25, £30, £40, £50, £100, £200, £300, £500 and £1000 denominations. Very few examples are in private hands. Notes from Bank of England branches other than London were also issued, but, again, are very rare.

BANK OF ENGLAND NOTES 1694 - 1928

No.	Signature/face value/details	Fine

Thomas Rippon 1829 - 1835:

REB61	£5	£10,000
REB62	£10	£18,000
	See note under Matthew Marshall section, below.	

Matthew Marshall 1835 - 1864:

REB91	£5, hand written signature	£5000
REB92	£5, printed signature	£5000
REB93	£5, signature in watermark	£5000
REB94	£10, hand written signature	£10,000
REB95	£10, printed signature	£10,000
REB96	£10, signature in watermark	£10,000

Marshall and Rippon notes were also issued in £20, £30, £40, £50, £100, £200, £300, £500 and £1000 denominations. Very few examples are in private hands. Notes from Bank of England branches other than London were also issued, but, again, are very rare.

William Miller 1864 - 1866:
(none bear his signature, and the notes are instead signed by the bank officials: W. P. Gattie, T. Kent or C. T. Whitmel)

REB111	£5, hand written signature	£8000

During Miller's time as chief cashier notes were also issued in £10, £20, £50, £100, £200, £300, £500 and £1000 denominations. None are known in private hands. Notes from Bank of England branches other than London were also issued, but, again, none are known in private hands.

George Forbes 1866 - 1873:
(Early notes were signed by a bank official and can only be identified as a Forbes by the date)

REB121	£5, signed by a member of his staff	£4000
REB122	£5, printed 'Geo Forbes' signature	£10,000
REB123	£10, signed by a member of his staff	-
REB124	£10, printed 'Geo Forbes' signature	-
REB124	£10, as above. VF at auction 2003: £7,000	

Forbes' notes were also issued in £20, £50, £100, £200, £300, £500 and £1000 denominations. None are known in private hands. Notes from Bank of England branches other than London were also issued, but, again, none are known in private hands.

BANK OF ENGLAND NOTES 1694 - 1928

No.		Signature/face value/details	Fine	

Frank May 1873 - 1893:

REB141	£5		£3,000
REB142	£10		£4,000
		See note under Horace George Bowen section, below.	

No.		Signature/face value/details	Fine	VF

Horace George Bowen 1893 - 1902:

| REB151 | £5 | | £3000 | £5000 |
| REB152 | £10 | | £6000 | £10,000 |

Bowen and May notes were also issued in £20, £50, £100, £200, £300, £500 and £1000 denominations. Very few are known in private hands. Notes from Bank of England branches other than London were also issued, but, again, very few are known in private hands.

No.	Signature/face value/details	Fine	VF	EF

John Gordon Nairne 1902 - 1918:

REB160	£1, undated, A/1 000000 serial			(UNC) £7000
REB161	£5, London, pre 1911 (1909 noted 2000)		£600	£900
	£5, London, later than 1911		£400	£600
	£5, provincial branches			£600+
REB162	£10, later than 1911		£600	£1000
REB163	£20, London or Manchester	£900	£2200	£4000
	Other branches are rare			
REB164	£50, London or Manchester	£900	£2200	£4000
	Other branches			£5000+
REB165	£100, London or Manchester		£2000	£3800
	Other branches are rare			
REB166	£200			-
REB167	£500			-
REB168	£1000, Manchester 1911		£12,000	

REB161

REB171

BANK OF ENGLAND NOTES 1694 - 1928

No.	Signature/face value/details	Fine	VF	EF
	Ernest Musgrave Harvey 1918 - 1925:			
REB171	£5, London	£130	£300	£2500
	Provincial notes are scarcer, recently noted are:			
	£5, Hull 1919		£700	
	£5, Leeds 1919		£500	
	£5, Liverpool			£850
	£5, Manchester 1920		£500	£900
	£5, Newcastle 1919		£900	£1400
	£5, Plymouth 1925		UNC: £2500	
REBS171	£5, Specimen 01/Q 0000 (Duggleby 7th Edition)		£3500	
REB172	£10, London 1918 - 1922			£650
	£10, London 1923 - 1925			£650
REB173	£20	£600	£1100	£2400
REB174	£50, Manchester	£900	£1500	
REB175	£100	£900	£1200	£2500
REB176	£200			£15,000
REB177	£500			£17,000
REB178	£1000, very rare			

Early Bank of England notes are found to have one straight cut edge and three untrimmed, or 'torn' edges. The fact they were printed in pairs means that half of them have a left cut edge, whilst the other half have a right cut edge.

BANK OF ENGLAND NOTES from 1928

The Modern Series

In November 1928, under the *Currency and Banknote act* of that year, the Bank of England assumed all responsibility for issuing bank notes. On the 22nd November 1928 the 'Series A' green One Pound notes and red/brown Ten Shilling notes were introduced to circulate with the existing higher denomination white notes (the production of which had not ben affected by the Treasury taking the roll of printing the lower denomination notes). In July 1933 the last of the 10 Shilling and One Pound Treasury notes were withdrawn from circulation.

There was serious intention to replace the silver coins in circulation with notes to the value of One Shilling, Two Shillings, and Five Shillings. The designs for each note were to be identical, front and back, without watermark and not numbered. A thread however, was to be incorporated.

The One Shilling, Two Shilling and Five Shilling notes were not taken beyond the proof stage. Notes for Two Shillings and Sixpence (Half a Crown) and for Five Shillings (a Crown) were produced in large numbers and distributed to a number of banks just in case.

None were put into circulation and they were all recalled to be pulped. However, some of the Half Crown and Crown notes did escape, and are very rare.

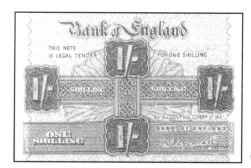

One Shilling

Two Shillings

Images on this page used with permission of Pam West Britishnotes.

BANK OF ENGLAND NOTES from 1928

No.	Date	Signature/face value/details	VF	EF

K. O. Peppiatt (1934 - 1949):

The Half Crown (Two Shillings and Sixpence)
Black on pale blue - 114 x 73mm - 4 $^1/_2$ x 2 $^7/_8$ in
Four 2/6 symbols, design the same on both sides

RB1	1941	No serial numbers	£4000	£6500

Five Shillings (a Crown)
Olive green on pale pink - 114 x 73mm - 4 $^1/_2$ x 2 $^7/_8$ in
Large central 5, design the same on both sides

RB2	1941	No serial numbers	£4000	£6500

Two Shillings and Six Pence (Half a Crown)

Five Shillings (A Crown)

Images on this page used with permission of Pam West Britishnotes.

BANK OF ENGLAND NOTES from 1928

No.	Start date	Signature/face value/details	Fine	VF	EF	AUNC

Ten Shillings - Britannia type
Series A - Red/brown - 137-139 x 78mm - 5 $\frac{1}{2}$ x 3 $\frac{1}{16}$ in

C. P. Mahon (1925 - 1929):

No.	Start date	Signature/face value/details	Fine	VF	EF	AUNC
RB3	1928 (Nov)	LNN (A , then Z to V backwards)				
		A01	£250	£500	£1000	
		Z01	£150	£350	£650	£1100
		Z- -		£90	£200	£250
		Y- -, X- -, W- -	£40	£70	£100	£180
		V02 (noted 2000)			£900	
		V- -		£475	£900	
RBS3	1928	A00 000000 SPECIMEN		£1,100 GVF in 2003		

B. G. Catterns (1929 - 1934):

No.	Start date	Signature/face value/details	Fine	VF	EF	AUNC
RB5	1930 (July)	LNN (V14 to K99 without P)				
		V14		£800		
		V- -		£80	£200	£320
		V98 (noted 2003)		£130		
		U- - to L- - (without P)		£40	£80	£170
		K- -		£80	£180	£320

RB5

Reverse common to all from RB3 to RB20 (in Mauve of course for RB10)

BANK OF ENGLAND NOTES from 1928

No.	Start date	Signature/face value/details	VF	EF	AUNC

Ten Shillings - Britannia type (continued)

Series A - **Red/brown** - 137-139 x 78mm - 5 $^1/_2$ x 3 $^1/_{16}$ in

K. O. Peppiatt (1934 - 1949):

No.	Start date	Signature/face value/details	VF	EF	AUNC
RB7	1934 (Oct)	LNN (J01 to A99 without F, G or I)			
		J01	£420	£850	
		J- -	£40	£100	£160
		H- - to B - - (without F or G)	£30	£70	£120
		A- -	£35	£90	£160
RBS7		Q00 000000 SPECIMEN		£850	£1300
RB8		NNL (01Z to 42O without P, Q, V)			
		01Z	£200	£450	
		- -Z	£40	£100	£180
		- -Y to - -O (without P, Q, V)	£30	£70	£170

RB8

RB10 - Emergency Mauve Issue

Series A - **Mauve** - 137-139 x 78mm - 5 $^1/_2$ x 3 $^1/_{16}$ in
With metal thread, wartime emergency issue.

No.	Start date	Signature/face value/details	VF	EF	AUNC
RB10	1940 (April)	LNNL (Z01D to A99D without F, G, I, P, Q or V. Z01E to X21E)			
		Z01D	£120	£240	£350
		Z- -D	£25	£45	£90
		Y- -D to B- -D (without F, G, I, P, Q or V)			
			£20	£34	£65
		A- -D	£25	£55	£80
		Replacement Prefix T- -D	£180		
		No serial number (noted 2002)	£320		

BANK OF ENGLAND NOTES from 1928

No.	Start date	Signature/face value/details	VF	EF	AUNC

Ten Shillings - Britannia type (continued)

Series A - **Mauve** - 137-139 x 78mm - 5 $^1/_2$ x 3 $^1/_{16}$ in
With metal thread, wartime emergency issue.

K. O. Peppiatt (1934 - 1949):

RB10   1940 (April)   LNNL (Z01D to A99D without F, G, I, P, Q or V. Z01E to X21E)

Z01E		£130	£350	£500
Z- -E and Y- -E		£30	£65	£80
X- -E		£40	£85	£125

Y23E 343210 (noted 2003) 2 notes with same No. £200

Series A - back to **Red/brown** - 138-140 x 78mm - 5 $^1/_2$ x 3 $^1/_{16}$ in
Without thread in order to use up pre emergency issue paper.

RB12   1948 (June)   NNL (50O to 70O and then 05L - 71L)

- -O		£60	£140	£260
- -L		£55	£120	£280

RBS12   SPECIMEN Q00 000000   £900

RB14   1948 (Oct)   NNL, as RB12 but **with** security thread. (71L to 91E without F, G or I)

71L			£450	
- -K to - -H (without I)		£20	£50	£90
- -E		£30	£70	£130

RB15   NNL, Replacement notes (01A to 03A)

01A		£700	£1300	
02A		£400	£700	
03A	£450	£900		

RB14

BANK OF ENGLAND NOTES from 1928

No.	Start date	Signature/face value/details	VF	EF	UNC

Ten Shillings - Britannia type (continued)
Series A - Red/brown - 137-139 x 78mm - 5 $^1/_2$ x 3 $^1/_{16}$ in

P. S. Beale (1949 - 1955):

No.	Start date	Signature/face value/details	VF	EF	UNC
RB16	1950 (March)	NNL (92E to 92B)			
		92E	£200	£550	£800
		- -E	£100	£200	£320
		- -D, - -C and - -B	£35	£70	£130
RBS16		SPECIMEN		£850	
RB17		LNNL (Z01Z to D85Z without F, G, I, P, Q or V)			
		Z01Z	£80	£460	£820
		Z- -Z	£18	£40	£70
		Y- -Z to E- -Z (without F, G, I, P, Q or V)	£15	£25	£60
		D- -Z	£18	£30	£65
RB18		Replacement notes (04A - 35A)			
		04A	£500	£900	
		- -A	£80	£150	£280

RB16

L.K. O'Brien (1955 - 1962):

No.	Start date	Signature/face value/details	VF	EF	UNC
RB19	1955 (Nov)	LNNL (D86Z to A99Z. Then Z01Y to A99Y without F,G, I, P,Q and V. Then Z01X to Y25X)			
		D86Z	£60	£150	£300
		D- -Z	£25	£70	£100
		C- -Z to A- -Z	£10	£18	£40
		A99Z	£30	£80	£130
		Z01Y	£45	£85	£180
		Z- -Y	£7	£20	£35
		Y- -Y to A- -Y without F,G, I, P,Q and V	£7	£15	£30
		N- -Y miscut EF (noted 2001)		£150	

BANK OF ENGLAND NOTES from 1928

No.	Start date	Signature/face value/details	VF	EF	UNC

Ten Shillings - Britannia type (continued)
Series A - Red/brown - 137-139 x 78mm - 5 $^1/_2$ x 3 $^1/_{16}$ in

L.K. O'Brien (1955 - 1962) continued:

No.	Start date	Signature/face value/details	VF	EF	UNC
RB19	1955 (Nov)	LNNL (Z01X to Y25X)			
		Z- -X	£11	£20	£40
		Y- -X	£11	£20	£40
RBS19		SPECIMEN		£600	£1125
RB20		Replacement notes (35A to 69A)			
		35A	£160	£400	
		- -A	£40	£95	£180

RB19

RB20

BANK OF ENGLAND NOTES from 1928

No.	Start date	Signature/face value/details	Fine	VF	EF	UNC

Ten Shillings - H.M. The Queen Portrait type
Series C - Red/brown - 140 x 66.7mm - 5 $^1/_2$ x 2 $^5/_8$ in

L.K. O'Brien (1955 - 1962):

No.	Start date	Signature/face value/details	Fine	VF	EF	UNC
RB21	1961 (Oct)	LNN (A01 to K64 without F, G or I)				
		A01	£15	£30	£75	£150
		A- -	£3	£6	£9	£12
		B- - to J- - (without F, G or I)	£2	£6	£8	
		K- -	£5	£10	£20	
RBS21		A00 000000 SPECIMEN				£750
RB22		(M01 to M18 replacement notes)				
		M01	£35	£110	£250	
		M- -		£50	£95	

RB21

Reverse common to all from RB21 to RB28

J.Q. Hollom (1962 - 1966):

No.	Start date	Signature/face value/details	Fine	VF	EF	UNC
RB23	1963 (April)	LNN (K65 to Z99 without M, O, P, Q or V)				
		K65	£45	£180	£300	
		K- -	£10	£16	£36	
		L- - to Y- - without M, O, P, Q or V		£4	£7	
		Z- -		£8	£16	
		Z98 noted 2003		£12	£22	

BANK OF ENGLAND NOTES from 1928

No.	Start date	Signature/face value/details	VF	EF	UNC

Ten Shillings - H.M. The Queen Portrait type
Series C - Red/brown - 140 x 66.7mm - 5 $^1/_2$ x 2 $^5/_8$ in

 **RB23**

RB24

J.Q. Hollom (1962 - 1966):

RB24	1963 (April)	NNL (01A to 26R without F, G, I, M, O, P or Q)			
		01A	£35	£120	£220
		- -A	£2	£6	£12
		- -B to - -N without F, G, I, M		£4	£8
		- -R		£18	£32
RB25		LNN (M19 to M55 replacement notes)			
		M19	£60	£200	
		M- -	£11	£25	£50
		M55		£100	£250

J.S. Fforde (1966 - 1970):

RB26	1967 (Feb)	NNL (26R to 99Z without V)			
		26R	£40	£200	
		- -R		£10	£16
		- -S to - -Y without V	£2	£6	£14
		- -Z		£8	£16
RBS26		SPECIMEN			£750

BANK OF ENGLAND NOTES from 1928

No.	Start date	Signature/face value/details	VF	EF	UNC

Ten Shillings - H.M. The Queen Portrait type
Series C - Red/brown - 140 x 66.7mm - 5 $^1/_2$ x 2 $^5/_8$ in

J.S. Fforde (1966 - 1970) continued:

No.	Start date	Signature/face value/details	VF	EF	UNC
RB27	1967 (Feb)	LNNL (A01N to D38N)			
		A01N		£85	£150
		A- -N	£2	£7	£15
		B- -N and C- -N			£10
		C01N (Coin)		Up to	£20
		D- -N		£4	£10
		D37N			£30
		D38N		£35	£70
RB28		Replacement note LNN (M56 to M80)			
		M56	£35	£95	£180
		M- -	£4	£8	£14
		M80		£10	£25

RB21 to RB27 feature interesting serial number prefixes, such as: H2O, CO2, O1L, C01N. These sometimes command a small premium.

RB27 with 'COIN' prefix

RB28

BANK OF ENGLAND NOTES from 1928

No.	Start date	Signature/face value/details	Fine	VF	EF	AUNC

One Pound - Britannia type
Series A - Green - 151 x 85mm - 5 $^{15}/_{16}$ x 3 $^{5}/_{16}$ in

C. P. Mahon (1925 - 1929):

RB31	1928 (Nov)	LNN (A01 to H32)				
		A01	£150	£500	£950	£1500
		A- -	£30	£70	£130	£210
		B- - to G- -		£50	£95	£180
		H- -		£80	£130	

Presented in parchment envelopes inscribed: 'BANK OF ENGLAND 22 November 1928' were 125 pairs of £1 and 10s notes with matching serial numbers. All are A01 - - - - - -
£7000

RBS31		A00 000000 SPECIMEN (noted 1999)				£1100

B.G. Catterns (1929 - 1934):

RB33	1930 (July)	LNN (H33 to Z99 without I, P, Q or V)				
		H33			£800	
		H- - to Y- - without I, P, Q or V	£8	£20	£40	£80
		Z- -		£35	£70	£120
		Z99 Higher than above prices, insufficient data				

RBS33		Q00 SPECIMEN				£950

RB34		NNL (01A to 99A)				
		01A	£80	£250	£450	
		- -A	£25	£65	£150	

RB33

BANK OF ENGLAND NOTES from 1928

No.	Start date	Signature/face value/details	Fine	VF	EF	AUNC

One Pound - Britannia type (continued)

Series A - Green - 151 x 85mm - 5 $^{15}/_{16}$ x 3 $^{5}/_{16}$ in

K.O. Peppiatt (1934 - 1949):

No.	Start date	Details	Fine	VF	EF	AUNC
RB36	1934 (Oct)	NNL (01B to 99Z without F, G, I, P, Q or V)				
		01B		£600	£1100	
		- -B	£12	£30	£60	£110
		- -C to - -Y		£15	£40	£80
		- -Z		£30	£60	£120
RBS36		SPECIMEN			£900	
RB37		LNNL (A03A to L39A without F, G or I)				
		A01A		£900		
		A- -A		£25	£60	£110
		B- -A to K- -A		£15	£35	£60
		L- -A		£20	£40	£70
		L39A		£60	£200	

RB36

RB42 Reverse - Showing the design common to notes RB31 - RB54

BANK OF ENGLAND NOTES from 1928

No.	Start date	Signature/face value/details	Fine	VF	EF	UNC

One Pound - Britannia type (continued)
Series A - **Blue** - 151 x 85mm - $5 \, ^{15}/_{16}$ x $3 \, ^{5}/_{16}$ in
With a metal thread.

K.O. Peppiatt (1934 - 1949):

No.	Start date	Signature/face value/details	Fine	VF	EF	UNC
RB41	1940 (March)	LNNL (A- -D, A- -E and A- -H)				
		A01D	£20	£80	£160	£280
		A- -D	£3	£15	£30	£40
		A01E	£18	£60	£130	£260
		A- -E and A- -H	£4	£10	£15	£25
		A01H	£4	£10	£130	£260
RBS41		SPECIMEN A00D 000000			£800	

The front and back of Guernsey Overprint note RBG37a. Background information on the next page.

BANK OF ENGLAND NOTES from 1928

One Pound - Britannia type (continued)

The Guernsey Overprint

When the Germans occupied the Channel Islands in WWII almost all the British Channel Island currency was hoarded by the inhabitants. Small change was short, so the Germans gave permission for the islanders to issue small denominations of their own to the total value of £5,000. To prevent potential damage to the economy, this was done subject to the withdrawal and handing over of £5,000 worth of English bank notes to the Germans. After the first £5,000, the islanders were still short of change, so, again, £5,000 of notes were withdrawn and handed to the Germans, and another £5,000 worth of small change was made for use on the island. The notes handed over were old notes that were due to be destroyed, and on both ocassions they were stamped '**Withdrawn from circulation**' with either the date: September 18th 1941, or November 10th 1941.

Please note that the Guernsey overprint section has been re-organised, and the reference numbers changed to incorporate a 'G' for Guernsey for easy identification. The two digits in the reference number refer to the note type that was overprinted.

No.	Start date	Signature/face value/details	Fine	VF	EF	AUNC
		Guernsey Overprints dated 18 September:				
RBG31a	**Mahon**	A- - to H- - (48 only)		£460	£920	
RBG33a	**Catterns**	H- - to Z- - (74 only)		£410	£720	
RBG34a	**Catterns**	- -A (5 only)		£2200		
RBG36a	**Peppiatt**	- -B to - -Z (328 only)		£370	£620	
RBG37a	**Peppiatt**	A- -A to L- -A (1,898)		£170	£360	£480
RBG41a	**Peppiatt**	A- -D (35 only) Blue type		£420	£720	
RBG42a	**Peppiatt**	C- -D (85 only) Blue type			£720	
		Guernsey Overprints dated 10 November:				
RBG37b	**Peppiatt**	E03A (79 only)		£390	£660	
RBG37c	**Peppiatt**	E15A (398 only)	£125	£250	£450	

The suffixes on the reference numbers above refer to the full stop after the overprint:
a: Has full stop after the '1941' on the front only.
b: Has full stop after the '1941' on front and back.
c: Has full stop after the '1941' on the back only

No.	Start date	Signature/face value	Fine	VF	EF	UNC

One Pound - Britannia type (continued)

Series A - **Blue** - 151 x 85mm - $5 \, ^{15}/_{16}$ x $3 \, ^{5}/_{16}$ in
With a metal thread.

K.O. Peppiatt (1934 - 1949):

RB42	1940 (Sep)	LNNL				
		(B01D to Z87D, B01E to W48E and B01H to X96H without F, G, I, P, Q or V)				

B01D		£5	£10	£25	£45
- 01D		£4	£8	£15	£35
B- -D to Z- -D without F, G, I, P, Q or V	£4		£12	£25	
Z87D, highest number found, so possibly of slightly higher value.					
B01E		£5	£10	£25	£45
B- -E to W- -E without F, G, I, P, Q or V	£4		£12	£25	
B01H		£5	£10	£25	£45
B- -H to X- -H without F, G, I, P, Q or V	£4		£12	£25	
Replacement notes S- -D, S- -E, S- -H	£140		£300		

RBS42		SPECIMEN A00D			£800	

NOTE -   Back to the **Green** type, without the metal thread.
Sizes as previous type

RB44	1948 (June)	LNNL (R01A to S48A)				

R01A		£25	£85	£200	£380
R- -A			£20	£40	£65
S01A		£10	£45	£90	£180
S- -A			£20	£40	£65

RB42

BANK OF ENGLAND NOTES from 1928

No.	Start date	Signature/face value/	Fine	VF	EF	UNC

One Pound - Britannia type (continued)
Series A - **Green** - 151 x 85mm - $5\,^{15}/_{16}$ x $3\,^{5}/_{16}$ in
<u>With</u> a metal thread.

K.O. Peppiatt (1934 - 1949):

NOTE -   The prefixes of RB44 and RB46 do overlap. The metal thread, or absence thereof are the only means of differentiating these otherwise identical types.

RB46   1948 (Sep)   LNNL (S39A to Z99A and A01B to H36B without V, F or G)

	Fine	VF	EF	UNC
S39A			£600	
S- -A		£10	£35	£60
S99A (noted 1999)			£75	
T- -A to Y- -A without V	£4	£10	£25	
Z- -A	£3	£6	£25	£45
A01B	£10	£30	£180	£280
A- -B			£20	£50
B- -B to H- -B without F or G	£5	£10	£20	
H33B to H35B tend to be higher in value, often double H- -B				
H36B	£25	£60	£140	

RB46

RB47   LNNL (S01S to S09S, replacement notes)

	Fine	VF	EF	UNC
S01S			£320	£460
S- -S				£180

BANK OF ENGLAND NOTES from 1928

No.	Start date	Signature/face value	Fine	VF	EF	UNC

One Pound - Britannia type (continued)
Series A - Green - 151 x 85mm - 5 $^{15}/_{16}$ x 3 $^{5}/_{16}$ in

P.S. Beale (1949 - 1955):

No.	Start date	Signature/face value	Fine	VF	EF	UNC
RB51	1950 (March)	LNNL (H37B to Z99B, A01C to Z99C and A01J to L63J without F, G, I, P, Q or V)				
		H37B	£40	£120	£280	£500
		H- -B		£6	£20	£35
		H99B (noted 2003)			UNC:	£60
		- 01B			£10	£20
		J- -B to Z- -B without P, Q or V	£3		£6	£12
		Z98B and Z99B values a little higher				
		A01C	£8	£20	£60	£200
		A- -C		£4	£9	£25
		- 01C		£5	£10	£20
		B- -C to Y- -C without F, G, I, P, Q or V	£4	£8		£14
		Z- -C		£6	£15	£30
		A01J		£20	£60	£200
		A- -J			£8	£25
		B- -J to K- -J without F, G or I	£3		£6	£20
		L- -J		£5	£10	£20
		L63J		£35	£120	£220
RBS51		SPECIMEN				£800
RB52		LNNL (S10S to S70S, replacement notes)				
		S10S	£200	£310		£460
		up to S24S			£35	£70
		S70S			£250	£520

RB51

S 48S 265220 RB52 - Serial Number

BANK OF ENGLAND NOTES from 1928

No.	Start date	Signature/face value	Fine	VF	EF	UNC

One Pound - Britannia type (continued)

Series A - Green - 151 x 85mm - 5 $^{15}/_{16}$ x 3 $^{5}/_{16}$ in

L. K. O'Brien (1955 - 1962):

No.	Start date	Signature/face value	Fine	VF	EF	UNC
RB53	1955 (Nov)	LNNL (L64J to Z99J, A01K - Z99K and A01L to K13L without F, G, I, P, Q or V)				
		L64J	£60	£160	£260	
		L- -J to Z- -J without P, Q or V	£4	£12	£18	
		- 01 -	£6	£15	£30	
		Z99J		£80	£140	
		A01K	£30	£90	£170	
		A- -K	£6	£18	£24	
		B- -K to Y- -K without F, G, I, P, Q or V	£4	£12	£18	
		- 01 -	£4	£6	£12	
		Z- -K	£6	£18	£24	
		A01L	£30	£90	£170	
		A- -L		£20	£40	
		A- -L 000007 (or other very low numbers)	£40			
		B- -L to J- -L without F, G or I	£4	£12	£18	
		K- -L	£10	£25	£60	
		K13L	£40	£200	£350	
RBS53		SPECIMEN			£650	£1200
RB54		LNNL (S71S to S99S and S01T to S23T replacement notes)				
		S71S	£60	£160	£350	
		S73S	£15	£40	£70	
		S99S			£350	
		S01T	£60	£220	£400	
		S- -T			£40	£80
		S23T			£400	

RB53

BANK OF ENGLAND NOTES from 1928

One Pound - H.M. The Queen Portrait type
Series C - Green - 151 x 71.8mm - 6 x 2 $^1/_2$ in
No series B £1 notes were issued, see bottom of page 55.

RB65

**RB65 Reverse -
Common to all notes
RB61 - RB84**

No.	Start date	Signature/face value	Fine	VF	EF	UNC
		L. K. O'Brien (1955 - 1962):				
RB61	1960 (March)	LNN (A01 to Z99 without F, G, I, M, O, P, Q or V)				
		A01		£60	£130	£280
		A- -		£3	£10	£16
		B- - to Y- - without F, G, I, M, O, P, Q or V	£3	£6		
		- 01			£5	£10
		Z- -		£2	£8	£18
RBS61		A00 000000				£750
RB62		NNL (01A to 99Z without F, G, I, M, O, P, Q or V)				
		01A		£60	£130	£280
		- -A		£4	£10	£16
		- -B to - -Y without F, G, I, M, O, P, Q or V	£3	£6		
		01 -			£5	£10
		- -Z			£5	£10
RB63*		LNNL (A01N, A05N and A06N, experimental notes, with 'R' on reverse.)				
		A01N	£70	£180	£350	

A05N thought to be the rarest of the three prefixes.
* Formerly Number RB63R

BANK OF ENGLAND NOTES from 1928

No.	Start date	Signature/face value	Fine	VF	EF	UNC

One Pound - H.M. The Queen Portrait type (cont)
Series C - Green - 151 x 71.8mm - 6 x 2 $^1/_2$ in

L. K. O'Brien (1955 - 1962):

No.	Start date	Signature/face value	Fine	VF	EF	UNC
RB64	1960 (March)	LNNL (B01N to B76N)				
		B01N			£100	£200
		B- -N			£15	£30
RB65		LNN (M01 to M68, replacement notes)				
		M01	£25	£40	£160	£360
		M- -			£16	£34

J. Q. Hollom (1962 - 1966):

No.	Start date	Signature/face value	Fine	VF	EF	UNC
RB66 L- -T,	1963 (Feb)	LNNL (B- -N, C- -N to L- -N, A- -R to L- -R, A- -S to L- -S, A- -T to				

A- -U to L- -U, A- -W to L- -W, A- -X to K- -X and A- -Y without the usual F, G, I and a few other prefixes which were used in the production of RB70)

No.	Start date	Signature/face value	Fine	VF	EF	UNC
		B77N	£35	£60	£140	
		B- -N		£20	£40	£75
		C- -N to L- -N without F, G or I		£2	£4	£6
		A- -R to L- -R without F, G or I		£2	£4	£6
		A- -S to L- -S without F, G or I		£2	£4	£6
		A- -T to L- -T without D, F, G or I		£2	£4	£6
		A- -U to L- -U without F, G or I		£2	£4	£6
		A- -W to L- -W without C, F, G or I		£2	£4	£6
		A- -X to K- -X without F, G or I		£2	£4	£6
		A- -Y		£2	£4	£6
		B- -Y		£15	£40	£90
RBS66		SPECIMEN			£750	
RB67		LNN (M68 to M99 replacement notes)				
		M68		£40	£100	£180
		M- -	£5	£15	£30	£50
RB68		NNL (01M to 99M replacement notes)				
		01M	£20	£50	£100	£260
		- -M			£15	£35
RB69		LNNL (M01R - M08R replacement notes)				
		M01R			£140	£300
		M- -R			£50	£95

BANK OF ENGLAND NOTES from 1928

No.	Start date	Signature/face value	Fine	VF	EF	UNC

One Pound - H.M. The Queen Portrait type (cont)
Series C - Green - 151 x 71.8mm - 6 x 2 $^1/_2$ in

J. Q. Hollom (1962 - 1966):

RB70	1963 (Feb)	LNNL (A- -N, C- -W, D- -T and L- -X) With small 'G' on reverse to indicate that these notes were printed on a Goebel machine.				
		A09N				-
		A- -N	£4	£12		£20
		C- -W and D- -T	£3	£6		£12
		L- -X	£4	£8		£14
RB71		LNNL (M01N to M28N replacement notes) With small 'G' on reverse to indicate that these notes were printed on a Goebel machine.				
		M01N and M28N			£140	£340
		M- -N			£20	£60

RB72

Picture showing the location of the small 'G' on the reverse of the Goebel machine printed notes: RB70, RB71, RB74, RB78 and RB79. The reference numbers previously had a 'G' after them.

J. S. Fforde (1966 - 1970):

RB72	1967 (Feb)	LNNL (B11Y to L- -Y and A- -Z to L99Z without E, F, G and I. A couple of prefixes were used in the production of RB74				
		B11Y	£45	£180		
		B- -Y		£30		£50
		C- -Y to L- -Y and A- -Z to J- -Z without letters mentioned above.	£2	£5		£12
		- 01 -	£5	£10		£16
		L- -Z	£6	£12		£30
		L99Z				£260
RB72S		SPECIMEN A00 000000				£750

BANK OF ENGLAND NOTES from 1928

No.	Start date	Signature/face value	VF	EF	UNC

One Pound - H.M. The Queen Portrait type (cont)
Series C - Green - 151 x 71.8mm - 6 x 2 $^1/_2$ in

J. S. Fforde (1966 - 1970):

No.	Start date	Signature/face value	VF	EF	UNC
RB73	1967 (Feb)	LNNL (M09R to M50R replacement notes)			
		M- -R		£25	£50
RB74		LNNL (E01Y to E99Y and K01Z to K99Z) With small 'G' on reverse to indicate that these notes were printed on a Goebel machine.			
		E01Y		£160	
		E- -Y	£2	£4	£10
		K- -Z	£2	£4	£10
RB75		LNNL (M29N to M42N replacement notes) With small 'G' on reverse to indicate that these notes were printed on a Goebel machine.			
		M29N		£130	£270
		M- -N	£20	£40	£70
		M42N		£120	£260

RB76

No.	Signature/face value	VF	EF	UNC
RB76	LNNL (N01A to X42C without F, G, I, O, P, Q and V) A couple of prefixes were used in the production of RB78. These serials overlap with the early J. B. Page One Pound notes.			
	N- -A	£15	£30	£50
	N- -B to N- -L without F, G or I		£4	£6
	R- -A to R- -K without B, F, G or I		£4	£6
	S- -A to S- -L without F, G or I		£4	£6
	S89L (high, usually Page)			£70
	T- -A to T- -L without F, G or I		£4	£6
	U- -A to U- -H without E, F or G		£4	£6
	W- -A to W- -D		£4	£6
	X- -B		£4	£6
	X- -C		£30	£45

BANK OF ENGLAND NOTES from 1928

No.	Start date	Signature/face value/details	VF	EF	UNC

One Pound - H.M. The Queen Portrait type (cont)
Series C - Green - 151 x 71.8mm - 6 x 2 $^1/_2$ in

J. S. Fforde (1966 - 1970):

No.	Start date	Details	VF	EF	UNC
RB77	1967 (Feb)	LNNL (R01M to R53M, S01M to S72M, T01M to T04M and U01M - replacement notes) These serials overlap with the early Page One Pound notes.			
		R- -M	£5	£12	£20
		S- -M	£9	£18	£30
		T01M	£60	£300	£500
		T03M		£190	
		U01M		£300	£500
RB78		LNNL (R01B to R99B, R01L to R99L and U01E to U45E) With small 'G' on reverse to indicate that these notes were printed on a Goebel machine.			
		R- -B	£3	£8	£15
		R01L		£90	£160
		R- -L		£5	£10
		R99L		£45	£100
		U01E		£90	£160
		U45E			-

RB78

No.	Start date	Details	VF	EF	UNC
RB79		LNNL (N01M to N14M, T29M - T32M replacement notes) With small 'G' on reverse to indicate that these notes were printed on a Goebel machine.			
		N01M		£300	
		N- -M		£70	£130
		T- -M	£35	£60	£90	£180
		T29M and T32M		£90	£180

BANK OF ENGLAND NOTES from 1928

No.	Start date	Signature/face value/details	VF	EF	UNC

One Pound - H.M. The Queen Portrait type (cont)
Series C - Green - 151 x 71.8mm - 6 x 2 $^1/_2$ in

J. B. Page (1970 - 1980):

RB81a 1971 — LNNL (S87L, S89L, S90L, T- -B, T- -D to T- -H, T- -K and T- -L, U- -A to U- -D, U- -H, W- -A to W- -H without F or G)
Some of the prefix gaps are due to late Fforde notes being assigned them.

	VF	EF	UNC
S87L		£1200	
S89L and S90L		£800	
T- -B to T- -L without A, C, F, G, I or J		£3	£5
U- -A to U- -H without E, F or G		£3	£5
W- -A to W- -H without F or G		£3	£5

RB81b — LNNL (X- -A to Z84L without - - -F, - - -G or - - -I and numbered up to 84 only)

	VF	EF	UNC
X- -A to X- -L without F, G or I		£3	£5
Y- -A to Y- -L without F, G or I		£3	£5
Z- -A to Z- -K without F, G or I		£3	£5
Z- -L	£2	£5	£10

RB82 — LNNL (R44M to R99M, S32M to S98M, W01M to W84M, X01M to X60M replacement notes)

	VF	EF	UNC
R- -M		£20	£50
S- -M	£6	£10	£25
W- -M	£3	£10	£25
X01M Noted 2003			£135
X- -M	£3	£10	£25
X60M Noted 2006			£70

RB81b

No.	Start date	Signature/face value/details	VF	EF	UNC

One Pound - H.M. The Queen Portrait type (cont)
Series C - Green - 151 x 71.8mm - 6 x 2 $^1/_2$ in

J. B. Page (1970 - 1980):

RB83		LLNN (AN01 to HZ63 without O, P, Q or V) Some prefixes are not yet accounted for.			
		AN01	£50	£100	£220
		AN- -	£3	£10	£15
		AN94 Noted 2003			£40
		AR- - to AZ- - without V		£2	£6
		BN- - to BZ- - without O, P, Q or V		£2	£6
		CN- - to CZ- - without O, P, Q, or V		£3	£6
		DN- - to DZ- - without O, P, Q or V		£3	£6
		EN- - to EZ- - without O, P, Q or V		£2	£6
		HN- - to HZ- - without O, P, Q or V	£2	£3	£8
		HU- - 000001 Noted 2005			£180
		HZ62 Noted 2005		£60	£100
		HZ63 Noted 2005		£210	
RB84		LLNN (MR01 to MR41, MS01 to MS84, MT01 to MT23, MU01 to MU18 and MW01 to MW19 replacement notes)			
		MR01		£120	£250
		MS01		£120	£250
		MS84		£60	£130
		MT01		£60	£130
		MU01		£20	£40
		MW01		£50	£120
		MW19		£70	£140
		Others, numbered mid prefix		£6	£12

RB83

BANK OF ENGLAND NOTES from 1928

The replication of Series D and E Bank of England Bank Notes

The Bank of England have given written consent for Rotographic to reproduce its bank notes within this book. To meet the requirements of the Bank of England, with regard to the Series D and Series E notes (covering notes issued between 1971 to date), the word 'SPECIMEN' must appear twice on each note, diagonally, in specified places. So please bear in mind that the notes are not Specimen notes unless referred to as such in the text.

One Pound - The Queue / Isaac Newton

Series D - Mainly Green - 134.5 x 66.69mm - $5\,^5/_{16}$ x $2\,^5/_8$ in

No.	Start date	Signature/face value/details	VF	EF	UNC

RB85

RB85 Reverse - Common to RB85 - RB90, with slight colour enhancements for RB88 - RB90

J. B. Page (1970 - 1980):

RB85	1978 (Feb)	LNN (A01 to Z80 without F, G, I, M, O, P, Q or V)			
		A01 001205 (low serial, Noted 2004)			£60
		A01		£6	£15
		A- -		£3	£6
		B- - to Y- - without F, G, I, M, O, P, Q or V	£2	£2	£4
		Z01	£2	£9	£22
		Z- -	£3	£8	£16
RB85S		SPECIMEN A00 000000			£750

BANK OF ENGLAND NOTES from 1928

No.	Start date	Signature/face value/details	VF	EF	UNC

One Pound - The Queen / Isaac Newton (cont)
Series D - Mainly Green - 134.5 x 66.69mm - 5 $^5/_{16}$ x 2 $^5/_8$ in

J. B. Page (1970 - 1980):

No.	Signature/face value/details	VF	EF	UNC
RB86	LNN (M01 only. Replacement notes)			
	M01		£170	£320
RB87	NNL (01A to 80Y without F, G, I, M, O, P, Q or V)			
	01A		£20	£50
	- -A		£3	£6
	- -B to - -X without F, G, I, M, O, P, Q or V		£2	£5
	01 -		£3	£7
	10U (IOU)			£10
	10W (Isle of Wight)			£6
	- -Y		£4	£15
RB87E	81L Experimental (81A to 81Z not inclusive)			
	81A, 81C, 81D, 81E, 81H, 81K, 81N, 81R, 81S, 81T, 81U, 81W, 81X, 81Y		£200	£350
	81Z	£90	£250	£460

RB88 with 'COIN' prefix

No.	Signature/face value/details	VF	EF	UNC
RB88	LNNL (A01N to E84N)			
	A01N		£30	£60
	A- -N		£5	£14
	B- -N to D- -N		£4	£12
	E- -N		£8	£20
	E84N	£6	£12	£25

BANK OF ENGLAND NOTES from 1928

No.	Start date	Signature/face value/details	VF	EF	UNC

One Pound - The Queen / Isaac Newton (cont)
Series D - Mainly Green - 134.5 x 66.69mm - 5 $^5/_{16}$ x 2 $^5/_8$ in

D. H. F Somerset (1980 - 1988):

RB89		LLNN (AN01 to DY21 without O, P, Q or V)			
		AN01		£20	£42
		AN01 000481 Noted 2003			£130
		AR- - to AZ- - without V		£3	£5
		BN- - to BZ- - without O, P, Q or V		£3	£5
		CN- - to CZ- -		£2	£4
		DN- - to DX- - without O, P, Q or V		£3	£5
		DY01		£25	
		DY21		£35	

The last note produced was DY21 999997, the last 2 notes were spoilt in production. (Source: "Promises to Pay" by Derrick Byatt)

RBS89		SPECIMEN A00 000000			-
RB90		LLNN (MN04 to MN18, experimental notes)			
		MN- -		£900	
		Only 6 examples are known			

The £1 coin was introduced in 1983. £1 notes were de-monetized at midnight, March 11th 1988.

RB89

BANK OF ENGLAND NOTES from 1928

No.	Start date	Signature/face value	VF	EF	AUNC

Five Pounds - The 'White Fiver'
Black on white - 212 x 135mm - 8 $^5/_{16}$ x 5 $^5/_{16}$ in

C. P. Mahon (1925 - 1929):

No.	Start date	Signature/face value	VF	EF	AUNC
RB101	1925 (Apr)	London 1925	£320	£540	£720
		Hull 1927	£850		
		Leeds		£540	
		Liverpool		£640	

Mahon notes from the following branches also exist:
Manchester, Birmingham, Newcastle, Plymouth and Bristol.

No.	Start date	Signature/face value	VF	EF	AUNC
RBS101		SPECIMEN 001/Q	£2800		

B.G. Catterns (1929 - 1934):

No.	Start date	Signature/face value	VF	EF	AUNC
RB102	1929 (March)	London 1930/1931/1932	£260	£440	£700
		Leeds 1929	£350	£520	
		Manchester	£460	£610	
		Liverpool 1931	£420		

Catterns notes from the following branches also exist:
Hull, Birmingham, Bristol, Newcastle and Plymouth.

No.	Start date	Signature/face value	VF	EF	AUNC
RBS102		SPECIMEN		£2500	

RB102
Image courtesy of Pam West Britishnotes.

BANK OF ENGLAND NOTES from 1928

No.	Start date	Signature/face value/details	VF	EF	AUNC

Five Pounds - The 'White Fiver' (Continued)

Black on white - 212 x 135mm - 8 $^5/_{16}$ x 5 $^5/_{16}$ in

K. O. Peppiatt (1934 - 1949):

No.	Start date	Signature/face value/details	VF	EF	AUNC
RB103	1934 (May)	Birmingham		£880	
		Leeds 1937	£320		
		London 1937		£240	
		London 1944		£480	
		Liverpool		£520	
		Newcastle 1937		£820	
		Manchester	£410		
		Hull	£600		
		Notes were also issued in Bristol and Plymouth.			
RBS103		SPECIMEN 000/Q 00000		£2400	
NOTE		Now with metal thread on thicker paper.			
RB104 though	1945 (Oct)	LNN (E01 to L02 without F, G or I) Notes dated 1944 exist, although they were not issued until 1945.			
		E01	£160	£240	£400
		E- -		£140	
		H- -, J- - and K- -	£35	£140	£240
		L01 and L02	£160	£300	
RBS104		SPECIMEN E00 000000		£2000	

RB104

BANK OF ENGLAND NOTES from 1928

Operation Bernhard - The Nazi White Fivers

In an attempt to damage the British economy, the Nazis forged White Fivers in large numbers. They made one quite noticable 'improvement' to the British watermark, possibly so that they could accurately detect their own forgeries, particularly the top quality ones. Or, perhaps it was a cunning anti Nazi act by the team who laid the wires in the watermarking process. Or, perhaps even nothing more than a slight error. It is the one proven indicator which distinguishes the forgery from the genuine.

The white/clear line in the watermark of the counterfeit notes points to the centre of the triangular serif at the foot of the first 'N' of 'ENGLAND'. In genuine notes the line is off centre and more to the left of the serif when viewed the right way round. In the close-ups below, the 'N' has been magnified and intensified.

Counterfeit Note

Genuine Note

In Issue No.1, Volume 31, of the IBNS Journal there is an article by Lance K. Campbell in which he states quite adamantly that there were no Operation Bernhard (Nazi Forgery) notes for the denominations of £100, £500 or £1000. As always, however, there were other forgers at work. Identifying a forgery does not automatically prove it to be a 'Bernhard' example. The numbers used by the Nazis for the forged £5 notes were as follows:

A/128 to A/175 - A/281 to A/314 - A/317 to A/398
B/105 to B/131 - B/134 to B/182 - B/186 to B/237 - B/256 to B/279
J/373 to J/377

BANK OF ENGLAND NOTES from 1928

No.	Start date	Signature/face value/details	VF	EF	AUNC

Five Pounds - The 'White Fiver' (Continued)

Black on white - 212 x 135mm - $8\,^5/_{16}$ x $5\,^5/_{16}$ in
With metal thread, as RB103 but dated 1947.

K. O. Peppiatt (1934 - 1949):

No.	Start date	Signature/face value/details	VF	EF	AUNC
RB105	1948 (Sep)	LNN (L03 to M71)			
		L03	£90	£180	£360
		L- -		£120	£200
		M- -			£200
RBS105		SPECIMEN		£2300	

P.S. Beale (1949 - 1955):

No.	Start date	Signature/face value/details	VF	EF	AUNC
RB106	1949 (Dec)	LNN (M72 to Y70 without Q)			
		M- -			£190
		N- - to X- - without Q	£50	£90	£180
		Y- -			£200
RBS106		SPECIMEN		£1800	

RB106

BANK OF ENGLAND NOTES from 1928

No.	Start date	Signature/face value/details	VF	EF	AUNC

Five Pounds - The 'White Fiver' (Continued)
Black on white - 212 x 135mm - 8 $^5/_{16}$ x 5 $^5/_{16}$ in

L.K. O'Brien (1955 - 1962):

No.	Start date	Signature/face value/details	VF	EF	AUNC
RB107	1955 (Jan)	LNN (Y71 to Z99)			
		Y71	£75	£160	£350
		Y- -	£65	£100	£190
		Z- -	£65	£110	£200
RBS107		SPECIMEN Y71 000000		£1950	
RB108		LNNL (A- -A to D- -A)			
		A01A noted 2004		£850	
		A- -A	£70	£160	£240
		B- -A to D- -A		£160	£220

RB108

BANK OF ENGLAND NOTES from 1928

Five Pounds - Helmeted Britannia / Lion and Key
Series B - Blue/Green/Orange - 160 x 90mm - 6 $^5/_{16}$ x 3 $^9/_{16}$ in

The Bank had decided to replace the Series A notes as far back as 1931, but various reasons, including WWII, the Chief Cashier (Beale at that time) not being too struck on the designs, and not to mention a minor disagreement with the designer, delayed their issue. Eventually, in 1957 the only Series B note was issued, being the £5 helmeted Britannia type.

The two £5 symbols to the left show the difference between notes RB109 and RB110.

RB109

RB109 Reverse-Common to RB110 with the exception of the slightly different £5 symbols.

No.	Start date	Signature/face value/details	VF	EF	AUNC
		L.K. O'Brien (1955 - 1962):			
RB109	1957 (Feb)	LNN (A01 to E37) With solid blue reverse £5 symbols (see above).			
		A01		£180	£400
		A- -		£40	£80
		B01, C01, D01 and E01			£80
		B- - to E- -	£15	£35	£65
		E37 Noted 2007		£180	
RBS109		SPECIMEN A00 000000			£1150

BANK OF ENGLAND NOTES from 1928

No.	Start date	Signature/face value/details	EF	AUNC

Five Pounds - Helmeted Britannia/Lion and Key
Series B - Blue/Green/Orange - 160 x 90mm - 6 $^5/_{16}$ x 3 $^9/_{16}$ in

L.K. O'Brien (1955 - 1962):

RB110	1961 (July)	LNN (H01 to K45 without I) With lighter reverse £5 symbols (see images on page 55).		
		H01	£550	£900
		H- -		£65
		J- -		£55
		K- -	£35	£65
RBS110		SPECIMEN A00 000000		£1150

RB111 Reverse - Common to notes RB111 to RB118

No.	Start date	Signature/face value/details	VF	EF	UNC

Five Pounds - Queen portrait type
Series C - Blue - 140 x 84.8mm - 5 $^1/_2$ x 3 $^5/_{16}$ in
Reverse picture on previous page.

J.Q. Hollom (1962 - 1966):

No.	Start date	Signature/face value/details	VF	EF	UNC
RB111	1963 (Feb)	LNN (A01 to R19 without F, G, I, M, O, P or Q)			
		A01	£50	£110	£180
		A02 and A03		£30	£60
		B- - to N- -		£25	£40
		R- -	£45	£90	£135
RBS111		SPECIMEN A00 000000		£800	
RB112		LNN (M01 to M10 replacement notes)			
		M01	£165	£400	
		M- -		£160	£350

J.S. Fforde (1966 - 1970):

No.	Start date	Signature/face value/details	VF	EF	UNC
RB113	1967 (Jan)	LNN (R20 to Z99 without V)			
		R20	£40	£110	£200
		R- -	£12	£28	£55
		S- - to Z- - without V		£15	£35
		Z99		£160	
RBS113		SPECIMEN A00 000000 (Fforde)		£800	
RB114		LNN (M08 to M38 replacement notes)			
		M- -	£40	£110	£230

RB111

BANK OF ENGLAND NOTES from 1928

No.	Start date	Signature/face value/details	VF	EF	UNC

Five Pounds - Queen portrait type (continued)
Series C - Blue - 140 x 84.8mm - $5\,^1/_2$ x $3\,^5/_{16}$ in

J.S. Fforde (1966 - 1970):

No.	Start date	Signature/face value/details	VF	EF	UNC
RB115		NNL (01A to 40L without F, G or I)			
		01A	£60	£140	
		- -A		£20	£45
		- -B to - -K without F, G or I	£11	£18	£36
		- -L	£30	£70	£130
RB116		NNL (01M to 15M replacement notes)			
		01M		£180	
		- -M		£90	£190

J.B. Page (1970 - 1980):

No.	Start date	Signature/face value/details	VF	EF	UNC
RB117	1971	NNL (03C to 40L without F, G or I)			
		03C		£190	
		- -C		£35	£75
		- -D to - -E (- -J, - -K, L- - not seen)		£20	£55
RB118		NNL (04M to 18M replacement notes)			
		- -M		£150	£240

RB115

BANK OF ENGLAND NOTES from 1928

Five Pounds - The Queen / Duke of Wellington
Series D - Mainly blue - 145.5 x 77.8mm - 5 $^3/_4$ x 3 $^1/_{16}$ in

To meet the requirements of the Bank of England the word 'SPECIMEN' must appear twice on each series D or E note, diagonally, in specified places. Please also see the top of page 47.

 **RB121**

**Reverse -
Common to notes
RB119 to RB128**

No.	Start date	Signature/face value/details	VF	EF	UNC
		J.B. Page (1970 - 1980):			
RB119	1971 (Nov)	LNN (A01 to L94 without F, G or I)			
		A01 000067 Noted 2007		AUNC:	£340
		A01	£30	£95	£200
		A02		£30	£60
		A- - to K- - without F, G, or I		£10	£20
		L- -	£20	£70	£120
		Numbers printed on the reverse, Noted 2001 VF: £200			
		No serial number or prefix, Noted 2003 AVF: £160			
RBS119		SPECIMEN A00 000000		£850	
RB120		LNN (M01 to M05 replacement notes)			
		M01		£250	£470
		M- -		£180	£290

BANK OF ENGLAND NOTES from 1928

No.	Start date	Signature/face value/details	VF	EF	UNC

Five Pounds - The Queen / Duke of Wellington
Series D - Mainly blue - 145.5 x 77.8mm - 5 $^3/_4$ x 3 $^1/_{16}$ in

J.B. Page (1970 - 1980):

RB121	1973 (Aug)	NNL (01A to 95Z without F, G, I, M, O, P, Q or V) With small 'L' on the back of all, to indicate the printing method used.			
		01A 000101 Noted 2007			£350
		01A	£60	£120	£250
		- -B to - -Y without F, G, I, M, O, P, Q or V	£8	£15	£30
		94Z			£140
RBS121		SPECIMEN		£900	
RB122		NNL (01M to 08M replacement notes)			
		01M		£175	£420
		- -M		£160	£270
RB123		LLNN (AN01 to AZ- -, BN01 to BZ- -, CN01 to CZ- - and EZ04 to EZ56 without O, P, Q or V)			
		AN01	£50	£120	£260
		AN- - to AZ- - without AO, AP, AQ or AV		£12	£20
		BN- - to BZ- - wthout BO, BP, BQ or BV		£12	£20
		CN- - to CZ- - without CO, CP, CQ or CV		£12	£20
		EZ- -		£40	£80
		EZ56		£300	

EZ- - also occurs for RB124

RB123

BANK OF ENGLAND NOTES from 1928

No.	Start date	Signature/face value/details	VF	EF	UNC

Five Pounds - The Queen / Duke of Wellington
Series D - Mainly blue - 145.5 x 77.8mm - 5 $^{3}/_{4}$ x 3 $^{1}/_{16}$ in

D. H. F. Somerset (1980 - 1988):

RB124   1980 (June)   LLNN (DN01 to DZ- -, EN01 to EZ- -, HN01 to HZ- -, JN01 to JZ- -, KN01 to KZ- -, LN01 to LZ- - without O, P, Q or V. Also NA- - to NC90)

DN01 000432 Noted 2007		AUNC:	£215
DN01	£50	£85	£180
DN- -			£35
DN- - to DZ- - without DO, DP, DQ or DV			£18
DU- - With no signature (see picture below)		£90	£180
EN- - to EZ- - without EO, EP, EQ or EV			£18
EZ58 (Close to Page number)			£45
HN- - to HZ- - without HO, HP, HQ or HV			£18
JN- - to JZ- - without JO, JP, JQ or JV			£18
KN- - to KZ- - without KO, KP, KQ or KV			£18
LN- - to LY- - without LO, LP, LQ or LV			£18
LZ- -		£15	£30
LZ89			£100
*NA- - to NC- -			£20
NC01			£30
NC90			£50

* According to 'English Paper Money' (2006) by Vincent Duggleby (Reference No. B343) the prefix NA01 has not been seen. Please let us know if you have information on the NA01 prefix.

RB126   LL91 (AN91, BR91, CS91, DT91, EU91, HW91, JX91, KY91 and LZ91)

AN91 and LZ91	£700
BR91 to KY91	£600

RB124 - The type with missing signature.

BANK OF ENGLAND NOTES from 1928

No.	Start date	Signature/face value/details	VF	EF	UNC

Five Pounds - The Queen / Duke of Wellington
Series D - Mainly blue - 145.5 x 77.8mm - 5 $^3/_4$ x 3 $^1/_{16}$ in

D. H. F. Somerset (1980 - 1988):

No.	Start date	Signature/face value/details	VF	EF	UNC
RB127	1987 (July)	LLNN (RA01 to RC90 with thicker security thread)			
		RA01 000585 Noted 2007			£120
		RA01		£25	£60
		RA- -, RB- - and RC- -			£25
		RB01 and RC01			£30
		RC90			£60
RBS127		SPECIMEN RA00 000000			£900
		SPECIMEN A00 000000			£900

G. M. Gill (1988 - 1991):

No.	Start date	Signature/face value/details	VF	EF	UNC
RB128	1988 (Mar)	LLNN (RD01 to RL- -, SA01 to SE90 without RF, RG or RI)			
		RD01			£50
		RD- - to RL- - without RF, RG or RI	£10	£25	
		SA- - to SE- -	£10	£25	
		- -01	£12	£30	
		SE90			£95

1500 Wallets containing the 'last' Wellington £5 and 'first' Stephenson £5 with identical serial numbers were issued by the bank and were available 'new' for £110.00 up to about 2005. Please also see the information about the special issues on page 65.

RB128

BANK OF ENGLAND NOTES from 1928

No.	Start date	Signature/face value/details	VF	EF	UNC

Five Pounds - The Queen / George Stephenson

Series E - Mainly Green - 135 x 70mm - 5 $^{5}/_{16}$ x 2 $^{3}/_{4}$ in

G. M. Gill (1988 - 1991):

RB501* 1990 (June)   LNN (A01 to U17 without F, G, I, M, O, P or Q)

A01   £25
A- - to U- - without F, G, I, M, O, P or Q   £20
A06 example with differing serials, noted 1999   £100
Example missing olive green and orange colours. approx   £100
E67 Pair of consecutive notes missing much detail
to the right, with absent Queen. (see below)   approx   £400

* Formerly RB129

**RB501 Reverse -
Common to notes
RB501 - RB510**

**RB501 Error (The second
note of a consecutive pair)
- Much detail missing. A
very faint outline of The
Queen is just about vis-**

BANK OF ENGLAND NOTES from 1928

No.	Start date	Signature/face value/details	VF	EF	UNC

Five Pounds - The Queen / George Stephenson
Series E - Mainly Green - 135 x 70mm - 5 $^5/_{16}$ x 2 $^3/_4$ in

G. E. A. Kentfield (1991 - 1998):

RB502 1991 (Nov)   LNN (R01 to W18 without V)

		R01 000043 Noted 2007			£150
		R01			£35
		R- - to W- - without V		£7	£25
		W18			£80

See page 74 for £5 and £10 paired serial numbers.
Sets were also sold with matching £5 and £20 notes,
and matching £5, £10, £20 and £50 notes.

RB503   LLNN (AA01 to AB18) As RB502 but with bolder £5 denomination.

		AA01			£30
		AA- - and AB- -			£18

RBS503   SPECIMEN AA00 000000   £800

RB504   LLNN (AC01 to AL- -, BA- - to BL- -, CA- - to CL- -,
and DA- - to DC- -, all without -F, -G or -I. Also DL99 which was
a special run used only for notes destined for presentation
packs) As RB503 but printed using slightly different process.

		AC01			£95
		AC- - to AL- - without AF, AG or AI		£10	£15
		BA- - to BL- - without BF, BG or BI		£9	£12
		CA- - to CK- - without CF, CG or CI		£8	£10
		DA- -, DB- - and DC- -		£8	£20
		CL- - Column Sort		£20	£50

RB504b   LLNN (LL01 to LL45 replacement notes)

		LL- -	£50	£95	£140

RB504

BANK OF ENGLAND NOTES from 1928 - Cypher Notes

Notes with special serial numbers, to mark important occasions.

In a similar fashion to what the Royal Mint and Royal Mail have been doing for some time, in 1988 new opportunities were seen for the exploitation of Bank notes aimed at collectors (or people wanting to buy a gift for a collector!) in order to generate more profit.

In 1990 the first presentation packs were issued containing the 'last' series D and 'first' series E notes with matching serial numbers. At first this venture wasn't very well organised. Prices of the special notes became over inflated and some collectors and dealers were displeased about the way the notes were distributed.

In 1996 special notes started to be issued to mark important occasions, the first being the Queens 70th Birthday. The values of many of these notes now may not be as high as the original issue prices. As with similar 'commemorative' items (often for pretty obscure things!) from the Royal Mint and the Royal Mail, the secondary market is generally much quieter than the market for such items when they are new. This is partly because most of the people that want such items get them when they are new and then keep them. Therefore there are far fewer people looking for them 'second hand'. The fact that some of these special serial number issues were sometimes presented with coins from the Royal Mint, and stamps from the Royal Mail, tends not to affect their desirability.

Five Pounds - The Queen / George Stephenson
Series E - Mainly Green - 135 x 70mm - $5\,{}^{5}/_{16}$ x $2\,{}^{3}/_{4}$ in

G. E. A. Kentfield (1991 - 1998):

Cypher Note for the Queens 70th Birthday.
HM70 000001 to HM70 050000 including UNC 1996 £5 Coin.
Issue Price: £39.95

Cypher Note to mark the handing over of Hong Kong back to China
HK97 000001 to HK97 999999 (certain numbers missed out) UNC: £30
HK97 - - - - - - in mini sheet of 12   UNC: £150
HK97 - - - - - - in mini sheet of 35   UNC: £300

Cypher Note to honour the Queen's Golden wedding anniversary
HM50 000001 to HM50 005000 including UNC1997 £5 coin   -

Cypher Note for the occasion of reaching 1998!
YR19 980001 to (unsure)   -

Cypher Note for Prince Charles 50th Birthday
PW50 000001 to PW50 001000 including 1998 £5 coin.
Issue Price: £39.95

Cypher Note for reaching 1999.
YR19 9900001 to (unsure)   -

BANK OF ENGLAND NOTES from 1928

No.	Start date	Signature/face value/details	EF	UNC

Five Pounds - The Queen / George Stephenson
Series E - Mainly Green - 135 x 70mm - 5 $^5/_{16}$ x 2 $^3/_4$ in

Merlyn Lowther (1999 - 2003):

RB507 1998 (Jan) LLNN (EA01 to EJ45 without F, G or I and also CL01 to CL45)

			EF	UNC
	EA01			£30
	EA- - to EJ- - without F, G or I			£12
	EJ45		£20	£130
	CL- - Column Sort			£20

RB508 LLNN (LL01 to LL45 replacement notes)

	LL- -		£15	£45

RB509 2000 Cypher Note (see previous page) for the Millennium
YR20 000001 to (unsure)   -

RB510 Cypher Note for the Queen Mother's 100th birthday
QM10 000001 to QM10 010000 with £5 coin and stamp
Issue Price: £60

RB508

Five Pounds - The Queen / Elizabeth Fry
Series E - Mainly Green - 135 x 70mm - 5 $^5/_{16}$ x 2 $^3/_4$ in
Still series E, similar to previous. Same dimensions etc,
but with a new face on the reverse; that of Elizabeth Fry.

RB511 2002 (May) LLNN (HA- - to HH- -, DL- -, JA- -, JB- -, and XA- - to XK- -
without F, G or I)

	HA01	£15
	HA- - to HH- -, DL- - and JB- -	£8
	JA- - Without missing varnish on serial number	£12
	JA- - With missing varnish on serial number	£16
	JA90 Last prefix, with missing varnish	£30
	DL25 Column sort prefix	£20

RB511b XA- - to XK- - without F, G or I, Varnish trials   £90

RB512 LLNN (LL01 to LL90 replacement notes)
LL- -   £20

BANK OF ENGLAND NOTES from 1928

No.	Date	Signature/face value/details	EF	UNC

Five Pounds - The Queen / Elizabeth Fry
Series E - Mainly Green - 135 x 70mm - 5 $^5/_{16}$ x 2 $^3/_4$ in

No.	Date	Signature/face value/details	EF	UNC
RB513	2001	Cypher Note for the Victoria Centenary VR10 000251 to VR10 000650		-
RB514	2002	Cypher Note for the Queen's Golden Jubilee A mini sheet uncut pair of HM02 and HM03		-

Andrew Bailey (2003 - date):

RB515		LLNN (JB46 (traced) to JE- -. The JB prefix overlaps with Lowther. EL- - used for column sort.)		

JB46		£60
JB- - to JE- -		£8
EL- - Column Sort		£12

RB515

**Reverse - Common to
RB511 - RB515**

BANK OF ENGLAND NOTES from 1928

No.	Start date	Signature/face value/details	VF	EF	UNC

Ten Pounds - Large Black and White dated type
212 x 135mm - 8 $^1/_4$ x 5 $^1/_4$ in

C. P. Mahon (1925 - 1929):

RB151	1925 (Apr)	1925 London	£300	£800	
		1925 Liverpool		£1300	
		1925 Manchester		£1300	
		1927 London		£750	
		1927 Birmingham		£1100	

B. G. Catterns (1929 to 1934):

RB152	1929 (Mar)	1929 London	£280	£600	
		1929 Liverpool	£500	£800	
		1929 Birmingham		£1000	

K. O. Peppiatt (1934 to 1949):

RB153	1934 (Aug)	1934 London	£150	£500	£850
		1935 London		£500	£850
		1938 London		£500	£850
		1938 Liverpool		£800	
		1935 Birmingham		£900	

Ten Pound notes from the above cheif cashiers also exist from the Leeds, Hull, Newcastle, Plymouth and Bristol braches, but are rare.

RB153 Image courtesy of R J Marles.

BANK OF ENGLAND NOTES from 1928

No.	Start date	Signature/face value/details	VF	EF	UNC

Ten Pounds - The Queen / Lion holding key
Series C - Brown - 150 x 93mm - 5 $^5/_{16}$ x 3 $^5/_8$ in

J. Q. Hollom (1962 - 1966):

No.	Start date	Signature/face value/details	VF	EF	UNC
RB154	1964 (Feb)	LNN (A01 to A40)			
		A01 prefix, low number in leather folder with Bank of England letter (Noted 1990).			£1250
		A01		£70	£140
		A- -		£25	£50
		A40		£85	£170
RBS154		SPECIMEN A00 000000			£850

J. S. Fforde (1966 - 1970):

No.	Start date	Signature/face value/details	VF	EF	UNC
RB156	1967 (Jan)	LNN (A41 to A95)			
		A41	£75	£95	£170
		A- -		£30	£50
		A95		£100	£220
RBS156		SPECIMEN A00 000000			£900

J. B. Page (1970 - 1980):

No.	Start date	Signature/face value/details	VF	EF	UNC
RB158		LNN (A91 to C90)			
		A91		£900	
		B- - and C- -	£15	£25	£50
		C90			No data
RBS158		SPECIMEN B00 000000			£900

RB156 Image courtesy of Barry Boswell.

BANK OF ENGLAND NOTES from 1928

No.	Start date	Signature/face value/details	VF	EF	UNC

Ten Pounds - The Queen / Lion holding key
Series C - Brown - 150 x 93mm - 5 $^5/_{16}$ x 3 $^5/_8$ in

J. B. Page (1970 - 1980):

No.	Start date	Signature/face value/details	VF	EF	UNC
RB159	1971	LNN (M01 to M17 replacement notes)			
		M01			£220
		M- -			£60
		M17			No data

RB158
Image courtesy of
Pam West Britishnotes.

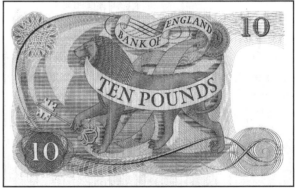

**Reverse common to
RB154 - RB159**
Image courtesy of Pam
West Britishnotes.

BANK OF ENGLAND NOTES from 1928

Ten Pounds - The Queen / Florence Nightingale
Series D - Mainly Brown - 151 x 84.87mm - 5 $^7/_8$ x 3 $^3/_8$ in

To meet the requirements of the Bank of England the word 'SPECIMEN' must appear twice on each series D or E note, diagonally, in specified places. Please also see the top of page 47.

RB167

Reverse common to RB161 - RB168

No.	Start date	Signature/face value/details		EF	UNC
		J. B. Page (1970 - 1980):			
RB161	1975 (Feb)	LNN (A01 to T20 without F, G, I, M, O, P or Q and also U34 and U39)			
		A01		£85	£170
		A- -		£22	£45
		A22 No signature	Approx	£50+	£150+
		B- - to S- - without F, G, I, M, O, P or Q		£25	£40
		U34 and U39 Somerset number note, with page signature in error.			
		U39 - - - - - - at auction in 1999			£632
RBS161		SPECIMEN A00 000000			£900
RBS161b		SPECIMEN (without 'SPECIMEN' overprinted) A00 000000	-		

BANK OF ENGLAND NOTES from 1928

No.	Start date	Signature/face value/details	VF	EF	UNC

Ten Pounds - The Queen / Florence Nightingale
Series D - Mainly Brown - 151 x 84.87mm - 5 $^7/_8$ x 3 $^3/_8$ in

J. B. Page (1970 - 1980):

RB162	1975 (Feb)	LNN (M01 to M50 replacement notes)			
		M01	£60	£140	£290
		M- -			£150
		M50	£35	£120	£240

D. H. F. Somerset (1980 - 1988):

RB163	1980 (Dec)	LNN (U01 to Z80 without V)			
		U01	£200	£400	£920
		U- -		£42	£85
		W- - to Y- -		£32	£68
		Z- -		£35	£75
		Z80		£400	
RB164		NNL (01A to 40L without F, G or I)			
		01A		£160	£340
		- -B to - -K without F, G or I		£25	£45
		- -L		£35	£50
		40L		£400	
RB165	1984 (Feb)	LLNN (AN01 to CR90 without -O, -P, -Q or -V) With small 'L' on reverse to indicate printing method.			
		AN01		£100	£220
		AN- - to AZ- - without O, P, Q or V		£18	£35
		BN- - to BZ- - without O, P, Q or V		£18	£35
		CN- - and CR- -		£18	£35
		CR67			£70
		CR90		£170	£300
RB166	1987 (July)	LLNN (CS01 to DN30 without CV- -) As RB165 but now with intermittent security thread (Stardust).			
		CS01		£60	£150
		CS- - to CZ- - without CV- -		£18	£40
		DN- -		£35	£68
		DN30		£350	

The small 'L' on the reverse of later series D £10 notes to indicate that they were printed using offset photo-lithography.

BANK OF ENGLAND NOTES from 1928

No.	Start date	Signature/face value/details	VF	EF	UNC

Ten Pounds - The Queen / Florence Nightingale
Series D - Mainly Brown - 151 x 84.87mm - 5 $^7/_8$ x 3 $^3/_8$ in

G. M. Gill (1988 - 1991):

RB167	1988 (Mar)	LLNN (DR01 to DZ- -, EN01 to EZ- -, HN01 to HZ- -, JN01 to JR60 without -O, -P, -Q or -V)			
		DR01		£25	£60
		DR- -			£35
		DS- - to DZ- -without DV- -			£30
		EN- - to EZ- - without EV- -			£30
		HN- - to HZ- - without HV- -			£30
		- -01			£35
		JN01		£15	£40
		JN- -		£40	£75
		JR- -			£75
		JR60		£300	

G. E. A. Kentfield (1991 to 1998):

RB168	1991 (Nov)	LLNN (KN01 to KN?? and KR01 to KR30)			
		KN01 Low serial			£150
		KN- -			£105
		KR- -			£60
		KR30		£40	£60	£115

BANK OF ENGLAND NOTES from 1928

No.	Start date	Signature/face value/details	EF	UNC

Ten Pounds - The Queen / Charles Dickens
Series E - Mainly Orange - 142 x 75mm - 5 $^9/_{16}$ x 2 $^{15}/_{16}$ in

G. E. A. Kentfield (1991 - 1998):

RB1001 1992 (Apr)   LNN (A01 to X40 without F, G, I, M, O, P, Q or V and also Y41 to Y96)

A01	First 400		£95
A01			£35
A- - to X- - without F, G, I, M, O, P, Q or V		£15	£30
X40			£80
Y- -			£80
Y96			No data

£10 series D and Series E with matched serials   £110
(Issue price new in March 2005)

RB1003

**RB103 Reverse
- Common to all
from RB1001 to
RB1006d**

RB1002   'Reclaimed' / 'B' Ream notes.
Unspoilt notes cut from partially spoilt sheets and separately
numbered. Duggleby lists M01 to M40 and Z90

M- -		£45	£130
Z90			£110

BANK OF ENGLAND NOTES from 1928

No.	Start date	Signature/face value/details	EF	UNC

Ten Pounds - The Queen / Charles Dickens
Series E - Mainly Orange - 142 x 75mm - 5 $^9/_{16}$ x 2 $^{15}/_{16}$ in

G. E. A. Kentfield (1991 - 1998):

RB1003	1993 (Nov)	LLNN (DA01 to DL- -, EA01 to EL- -, H01 to HK- -, JA01 to JK- -, KA01 to KK80 and also K99. Without -F- -, -G- - and -I- -) Now with bolder '£10' symbol on the left, and a second £10 symbol added to the right hand corner of the obverse and reverse.		
		DA01		£300
		DA- - to DK- - without DF, DG, or DI	£12	£25
		EA- - to EK- - without EF, EG or EI	£12	£25
		DL- - and EL- - (column sort)	£30	£60
		HA- - to HK- - without HF, HG or HI	£12	£25
		JA- - to JK- - without JF, JG or JI	£12	£25
		KA- - to KK- - without KF, KG or KI	£12	£25
		KK99 special run for presentation pack		£55
RB1003b		LLNN (LL01 to LL40 replacement notes)		
		LL- -	£48	£130

Cypher Notes - See page 65

RB1004		Cypher Note for the Queens 70th Birthday. HM70 000001 to HM70 002000 including UNC 1996 Silver proof £5 Coin. Issue Price: £97.50		
RB1004b		Cypher Note to honour the Queen's Golden wedding anniversary HM50 000001 to HM50 001500 including UNC1997 Silver proof £5 coin. Issue Price: £97.50		
RB1004c		Cypher Note for the occasion of reaching 1998. YR19 980001 to (unsure)		-
RB1005		Cypher Note for Prince Charles 50th Birthday PW50 000001 to PW50 000500 including 1998 Silver proof £5 coin. Issue Price: £97.50		
RB1005b		Cypher Note for reaching 1999. YR19 9900001 to (unsure)		-

BANK OF ENGLAND NOTES from 1928

No.	Start date	Signature/face value/details	EF	UNC

Ten Pounds - The Queen / Charles Dickens
Series E - Mainly Orange - 142 x 75mm - $5\,^9/_{16}$ x $2\,^{15}/_{16}$ in

Merlyn Lowther (1999 - 2003):

RB1006 1999 (Jan) LLNN (KL01, EL- -, KL- -, LA- - to LA80)

			EF	UNC
		KL01		£45
		EL01	£20	£75
		EL- -	£15	£45
		KA- - and LA- -	£12	£25
		LA80		£45
		Kentfield/Lowther notes with matched serial numbers		£55
		(Issue Price)		

RB1006b LLNN (LL01 to LL40 replacement notes)

LL- - £65 £140

Cypher Notes - See page 65

RB1006c Cypher Note for the Millenium.
YR20 000001 to YR 001500 -

RB1006d Cypher Note for the Queen Mother's 100th Birthday
QM10 000001 to QM10 000750 including
UNC 2000 Silver proof £5 coin -

BANK OF ENGLAND NOTES from 1928

Ten Pounds - The Queen / Charles Darwin
Series E - Mainly Orange - 142 x 75mm - 5 $^9/_{16}$ x 2 $^{15}/_{16}$ in

The design has been changed now on both sides (still series E). Charles Darwin now replaces Charles Dickens on the reverse, the '£10' symbols have been changed and a hologram has been incorporated.

RB1008

RB1008 Reverse - Common to notes RB1007 to current note, at time of writing

No.	Start date	Signature/face value/details	EF	UNC
		Merlyn Lowther (1999 - 2003):		
RB1007	2000 (Nov)	LLNN (AA01 to AH80 and EL- - without - F or - G. Also some - L prefixes) Copyright claim worded 'The Company' see page 78		
		AA01 007- - -		£40
		AA01		£30
		AA- - to AH- - without AF or AG		£20
		EL- - Column sort		£30
RB1007b		LLNN (LL01 to LL40 replacement notes) Copyright claim worded 'The Company' see page 78		
		LL- -	£35	£70

BANK OF ENGLAND NOTES from 1928

No.	Start date	Signature/face value/details	VF	EF	UNC

Ten Pounds - The Queen / Charles Darwin
Series E - Mainly Orange - 142 x 75mm - 5 $^9/_{16}$ x 2 $^{15}/_{16}$ in

The copyright claim on the obverse and reverse of notes RB1007 and RB1007b reads (incorrectly) 'THE GOVERNOR AND THE COMPANY OF THE BANK OF ENGLAND', as shown above in the left hand example. Notes from RB1008 onwards read correctly 'THE GOVERNOR AND COMPANY OF THE BANK OF ENGLAND' as shown in the right hand example.

Merlyn Lowther (1999 - 2003):

RB1008 2000 (Nov) LLNN (AA01 for presentation packs, AD- -, AJ- -, AK- -, and BA- - to CC77 (seen at time of writing) and MH- - to MM- - without MI or ML)
Copyright claim worded 'And Company' see above.
Notes in the CC- - range are known to overlap with RB1011.

	VF	EF	UNC
AA01			£50
AD- - Overlap prefix		£40	£80
AJ- - and AK- -			£20
BA- - to CC- -			£20
EL- - Column sort		£15	£25
MH- -, MJ- -, MK- - and MM- - Experimental Notes		£80	£200

RB1009 LLNN (LL01 to LL40 replacement notes)
Copyright claim worded 'And Company' see above.

	VF	EF	UNC
LL- -		£12	£30

Cypher Notes - See page 65

RB1010 Cypher Note for the Victorian era Centenary
QV10 000001 to QV10 050000 Plus UNC £5 coin   -

RB1010b Cypher Note for the Victorian era Centenary
VR10 000251 to VR10 000950 Plus Silver proof £5 coin -

BANK OF ENGLAND NOTES from 1928

No.	Start date	Signature/face value/details	EF	UNC

Ten Pounds - The Queen / Charles Darwin
Series E - Mainly Orange - 142 x 75mm - 5 $^9/_{16}$ x 2 $^{15}/_{16}$ in

Andrew Bailey (2003 - date):

RB1011   LLNN (CC41 (traced) to CK- -, without -F, -G or -I. Also DA- - to DJ- - and EL- - and HL- -)

Notes in the CC- - range are known to overlap with RB1008.

CC41 (lowest seen)		£150
CC- - to CK- - without CF, CG or CI		£15
DA- - to DJ- - without DF, DG or DI continuing...		£15
EL41 to EL80 Column Sort		£18
HL01 to HL40 Column Sort	£18	

RB1012   LLNN (Replacement notes LL only, up to LL40)

LL- -	£25

RB1011

BANK OF ENGLAND NOTES from 1928

No.	Signature/face value/details	VF	EF	AUNC

Twenty Pounds - Black and White type

Serial number large at upper right and repeated smaller lower right

212 x 135mm - 8 $^5/_{16}$ x 5 $^5/_{16}$ in

These three are rarely encountered. Valuations without market movements are estimates. Valuations presume London notes; branch notes will attract a substantial premium.

No.	Signature/face value/details	VF	EF	AUNC
RB171	**C. P. Mahon (1925 - 1929):**		£1250	£2300
RB172	**B. G. Catterns (1929 - 1934):**		£1100	£2000
RB173	**K. O. Peppiatt (1934 - 1949):**		£800	£1400

RB172

Image courtesy of Pam West Britishnotes.

BANK OF ENGLAND NOTES from 1928

No.	Start date	Signature/face value/details	VF	EF	UNC

Twenty Pounds - The Queen / Shakespeare Statue

Series D - Mainly Purple - 160 x 90mm - 6 $^1/_4$ x 3 $^1/_2$ in
Watermark is an image of The Queen.

No.	Start date	Signature/face value/details	VF	EF	UNC
RB174	1970 (July)	**J. S. Fforde (1966 - 1970):**			
		LNN (A01 to A05)			
		A01 000128 Noted 2007		AUNC	£460
		A01	£80	£160	£350
		A- -			£300
RBS174		SPECIMEN A00 - - - - - -			£1000
RB175		LNN (M01 only, replacement notes)			
		M01	£100	£220	£380
RB176	1970	**J. B. Page (1970 - 1980):**			
		LNN (A06 to D80)			
		A06	£120	£250	£500
		A- -			£100
		B- - and C- -			£80
		D01		£60	
		D- -		£40	£85
RB177		LNN (M01 to M04 replacement notes)			
		M01	£60	£150	£300
		M02 and M03			£160
		M04		£250	£450

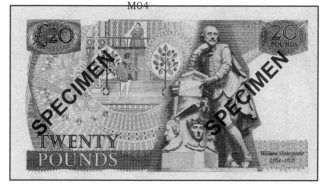

RB180 Reverse - Common to notes RB174 to RB181

BANK OF ENGLAND NOTES from 1928

No.	Start date	Signature/face value/details	VF	EF	UNC

Twenty Pounds - The Queen / Shakespeare Statue

Series D - Mainly Purple - 160 x 90mm - 6 $^{1}/_{4}$ x 3 $^{1}/_{2}$ in

No.	Start date	Signature/face value/details	VF	EF	UNC
RB178	1981 (Mar)	**D. H. F. Somerset (1980 - 1988):**			
		LNN (E01, H- - and J- - to J40)			
		E01	£150	£400	£660
		E02		£350	
		E- -		£120	£260
		H- - and J- -		£50	£100
		J40			£400
		No prefix or serial numbers			£250
RBS178		SPECIMEN A00 000000			-

RB180

No.	Start date	Signature/face value/details	VF	EF	UNC
RB180	1984 (Nov)	Watermark changed to image of Shakespeare and stardust (dotted) security thread introduced.			
		NNL (01A to 40K without F, G or I)			
		01A 000 - - -			£220
		01A			£180
		- -A to - -K without F, G or I		£40	£80
		40K			-
RBS180		SPECIMEN 00A 000000			£1000

BANK OF ENGLAND NOTES from 1928

No.	Start date	Signature/face value/details	VF	EF	UNC

Twenty Pounds - The Queen / Shakespeare
Statue

Series D - Mainly Purple - 160 x 90mm - 6 $^1/_4$ x 3 $^1/_2$ in

RB181	1988 (Mar)	**G. M. Gill (1988 - 1991):**			
		NNL (01L to 20X without O, P, Q or V)			
		01L	£40	£90	£160
		- -L to - -W without O, P, Q or V		£35	£80
		- -X			£100
		20X			£180
		Various errors noted:			
		40S Uncut base, with colour bars			£200
		Extra paper at bottom left			£175
		Numbers upside down			£400
		22R Missing much detail on both sides			£400
RB181 with RB128		£5 Series D SE69 and £20 Series D 20U			£100

RB181

BANK OF ENGLAND NOTES from 1928

No.	Start date	Signature/face value/details	EF	UNC

Twenty Pounds - The Queen / Michael Faraday
Series E - Mainly Purple - 149 x 80mm - 5 $^7/_8$ x 3 $^1/_8$ in

RB2000* 1991 (June)		**G. M. Gill (1988 - 1991):**		

LNN (A01 to U19 without F, G, I, M, O, P)

A01 early serial (up to 1000)		£75
A01		£70
A- - to U- - without F, G, I, M, O or P		£65

£20 Series D and £20 Series E with matching serials £195
(Issue price)

RB2000b* LNN (Z13 only. Special purpose notes)

Z13 -

*RB2000 was formerly numbered RB182.
*RB2000b was formerly numbered RB183.

RB2001 The 'B' Ream notes - Unspoilt notes taken from partly spoilt sheets and separately numbered. These prefixes are outside of the normal range (all above -70, others would be impossible to identify).

A71 to A97 noted	-
B74 to B82 noted	-
C -- noted	-

Reverse -
Common to notes
RB2000 to RB2004

BANK OF ENGLAND NOTES from 1928

No.	Start date	Signature/face value/details	EF	UNC

Twenty Pounds - The Queen / Michael Faraday
Series E - Mainly Purple - 149 x 80mm - 5 $^7/_8$ x 3 $^1/_8$ in

RB2001b		**G. E. A. Kentfield (1991 - 1998):**		
		LNN (M01 to M35 and Z01 to Z90 with gaps. M35) Experimental notes with prefixes outside the normal range.		
		M01 to M35 with gaps	£75	£150
		Z01 to Z35 with gaps	£85	£160
		Z90	£100	£200
RB2002	1991 (Nov)	LNN (E01 to W35 without F, G, I, M, O, P, Q or V. Later, old stock of prefixes A71 to A99, B71 to B99 and C71 to C99 were used)		
		E01 001- - -		£170
		E- -		£65
		A- -, B- - and C- -	£40	£140
		A71		£200
		E- - to L- - without F, G or I	£40	£65
		N- - to W - - without O, P, Q or V	£25	£65
		W35 999- - - (Noted 2002)		£130
		X- - and Y- -		£75
		X- - and Y- - Column Sort Only		£140
RB2002b		SPECIMEN X00 000000		£1100
RB2003	1993 (Sep)	LNN (X01 to Y70)		
		As above but with minor design changes including a '£20' symbol added to the top right of the reverse.		
		X01 0010- -		£140
		X- - & Y- -		£65
		Y01		£70
		Y70	VF: £60 (Noted 2002)	
RB2003b		Cypher Note for 1998 - YR19 98- - - -	-	
RB2004c		Cypher Note for 1999 - YR19 99- - - -	-	
RB2004	1994	LLNN (AA01 - AL- -, BA- - to BL- -, CA- - to CJ- - without -F, -G or -I and also CL- -)		
		AA01		£250
		AA- - to AL- -, BA- - to BL- - & CA- - to CJ- -	£25	£50
		CL-01 - CL40	£40	£110
		CL99 used in presentation packs only		£70
RB2004b		LLNN (LL01 to LL40 replacement note)		
		LL01 - LL40	£70	£140

BANK OF ENGLAND NOTES from 1928

No.	Start date	Signature/face value/details	EF	UNC

Twenty Pounds - The Queen / Michael Faraday
Series E - Mainly Purple - 149 x 80mm - 5 $^7/_8$ x 3 $^1/_8$ in

RB2004	1999 (Jan)	**Merlyn Lowther (1999 - 2003):**		
		LLNN (DA01 to DA80)		
		DA01		£105
		DA- -	£35	£80
		DA80		£95

Twenty Pounds - The Queen / Edward Elgar
Still Series E - Mainly Purple - 149 x 80mm - 5 $^7/_8$ x 3 $^1/_8$ in

RB2005	1999 (June)	LLNN (AA01 to AL- -, BA01 to BK- - and CA01 to CK- - without -F, -G or -I. Also DB- - (which was actually the first run to be printed) to DE- -)		
		AA01	£25	£45
		AA- - to AK- - without AF, AG or AI		£30
		AL- - Column sort prefix		£35
		BA01 to BK - - without BF, BG or BI		£35
		CA01 to CK- - without CF, CG or CI		£35
		DB- - to DE- - (traced to DE80, overlaps with Bailey)		£32

RB2005

Reverse - Common to notes RB2005 to date

BANK OF ENGLAND NOTES from 1928

No.	Start date	Signature/face value/details	EF	UNC

Twenty Pounds - The Queen / Edward Elgar
Still Series E - Mainly Purple - 149 x 80mm - $5\,^7/_8$ x $3\,^1/_8$ in

Merlyn Lowther (1999 - 2003):

No.	Start date	Signature/face value/details	EF	UNC
RB2006b	1999 (Jan)	LLNN (LL01 to LL40 replacement notes)		
		LL01		£140
		LL- -	£30	£60
RB2007		Cypher Note for the Millenium - YR20 00- - - - Also sold with Silver Crown		-
RB2008		Cypher Note for Queen Mothers 100th - QM10 00- - - - Also sold with Gold Proof Crown		-
RB2009		Cypher Note for 2001 - YR20 01- - - -		-
RB2010		Cypher Note for the Queens Jubilee With silver proof Crown. Issue price: With gold proof Crown. Issue price:		£100 £875
RB2011		Cypher Note for Queens coronation - QC50 - - - - - - - With Silver Crown. Issue price: With gold proof Crown. Issue price:		£99.50 £875
RB2012		**Andrew Bailey (2003 - present):**		
		LLNN (DE41 (traced) to DK- - without -F, -G or -I with Lowther overlaps in the DE- - range. Also EA- - to EH- -, without EF, EG or EI. BL- - column sort.)		
		DE41		£150
		DE- - to DK- -		£25
		EA- - to EH- -		£40
		BL- - Column Sort		£35
RB2012b		LLNN (LL01 to LL40 replacement notes)		
		LL- -		£50

No.	Start date	Signature/face value/details	EF	UNC

Twenty Pounds - The Queen / Adam Smith
Mainly Purple - 149 x 80mm - 5 $^7/_8$ x 3 $^1/_8$ in

RB2013   **Andrew Bailey (2003 - present):**

LLNN (AA- -, AB- -, AB- -, AC- -, AD- - AJ- - and AK- -. Also BA- -, BB- - and BC- -. Prefixes starting C?- - have not yet been seen but DD- - exists at the time of writing.

All are worth face value until more is known.

RB2013

BANK OF ENGLAND NOTES from 1928

No.	Start date	Signature/face value/details	VF	EF	AUNC

Fifty Pounds - Large White Type
Design on one side only - 212 x 135mm - 8 $\frac{5}{16}$ x 5 $\frac{5}{16}$ in

RB193
Image courtesy of Pam West Britishnotes.

C. P. Mahon (1925 - 1929):

RB191		London		£1100	£2000

B. G. Catterns (1929 - 1934):

RB192		London		£1100	£1600
		Manchester		£1300	

K. O. Peppiatt (1934 - 1949):

RB193		London		£600	£1100

No.	Start date	Signature/face value/details	VF	EF	UNC

Fifty Pounds   The Queen / Sir Christopher Wren
Series D   Multicoloured   169 x 95mm $6\,^5/_8$ x $3\,^3/_4$ in

RB194

RB194	1981 (Mar)	**D. H. F. Somerset (1980 1988):**			
		LNN (A01 to B90)			
		A01			£180
		A- - and B- -			£130
		B90		£130	£260
RBS194		SPECIMEN		£950	
RB195	1988	**G. M. Gill (1988 1991):**			
		LNN (C01 - D90, plus higher D- -, see below)			
		C01	£75	£200	£350
		C- - and D- -		£75	£140
		D90	£75	£130	£250

Some D- and E- prefixes of Gill exist. These notes were issued to replace spoilt Kentfields.

		D95		£100	
RB196	1991 (Nov)	**G. E. A. Kentfield (1991 - 1998):**			
		LNN (E01 to E30)			
		E01			£180
		E02 000006 (Noted 2003)		AUNC	£165
		E- -			£140
		E30			£180
		E30 With High Serial			£200

**Reverse
Common to
RB194   RB196**

No.	Start date	Signature/face value/details	EF	UNC
		Fifty Pounds The Queen / Sir John Houblon		
		Series E Mainly Red- 156 x 85mm $6\,^3/_{16}$ x $3\,^5/_{16}$ in		
RB5001	1994 (Apr)	**G. E. A. Kentfield (1991 - 1998):**		
		LNN (A01 to H- - without F- - or G- -. Also H99 and L- -)		
		A01 001000 or lower		£180
		A01		£145
		A- to H- without F- or G-		£95
		H99 From presentation packs only		£120
		L- Column sort prefix	£75	£130
		L35 (highest recorded)		-
		A- -, B- - and C- - Numbers over 70 (column sort)		£140
RB5001b		LLNN (LL01 to LL35 column sort notes)		
		LL- -	£90	£200

RB5004

BANK OF ENGLAND NOTES from 1928

No.	Start date	Signature/face value/details	EF	UNC

Fifty Pounds - The Queen / Sir John Houblon
Series E - Mainly Red- 156 x 85mm - $6\,^3/_{16}$ x $3\,^5/_{16}$ in

RB5002	1994 (Apr)	**G. E. A. Kentfield (1991 - 1998):**		
RB5002b		LNN (M- - experimental notes)		
		A99	£80	£140
		M01	£150	£300
RB5003		Cypher Note for Prince Charles' 50th - PW50 000- - - Issued with gold Proof £5 Coin. Price new:		£895
RB5004	1999 (Jan)	**Merlyn Lowther (1999 - 2003):**		
		LNN (J01, K- - to M35 and L- - for column sort)		
		J01 - Originally for presentation packs only		£150
		K- -		£80
		M01		£150
		M35		£180
		L- - Column sort		£100

Reverse - Common to notes RB5001 to date

RB5005	2007	**Andrew Bailey (2003 - Present):**		
		LNN (M01 to M??. Continuing)		
		M01		£150
		M- -		Face Value

BANK OF ENGLAND NOTES from 1928

No.	Start date	Signature/face value/details	VF	EF

One Hundred Pounds - Large White Type
Design on one side only - 212 x 135mm - 8 $^5/_{16}$ x 5 $^5/_{16}$ in

No.	Start date	Signature/face value/details	VF	EF
RB201		**C. P. Mahon (1925 - 1929):**		
			£1600	£2800
RB202		**B. G. Catterns (1929 - 1934):**		
			£1350	£2300
RB203		**K. O. Peppiatt (1934 - 1949):**		
		London	£880	£1600
		Liverpool	£1100	£2100

RB203
Image courtesy of Pam West Banknotes.

BANK OF ENGLAND NOTES from 1928

No.	Start date	Signature/face value/details	VF	EF

Two Hundred Pounds - Large White Type
Design on one side only.

| RB220 | | **C. P. Mahon (1925 - 1929):** | | |
| | | SPECIMEN only | - | |

Five Hundred Pounds - Large White Type
Design on one side only.

RB221		**C. P. Mahon (1925 - 1929):**	-	-
RB222		**B. G. Catterns (1929 - 1934):**	-	-
RB223		**K. O. Peppiatt (1934 - 1949):**	-	£7300

One Thousand Pounds - Large White Type
Design on one side only.

RB301		**C. P. Mahon (1925 - 1929):**	-	-
RB302		**B. G. Catterns (1929 - 1934):**	-	£24,000
RB303		**K. O. Peppiatt (1934 - 1949):**	-	£23,000

Larger Denominations

In the past larger denomination notes have been produced, but none that were intended for circulation. Notable are the Fifteen Thousand Pound notes that were issued to British Airmen in the 1991 Gulf War. The sum was paid to the airmen on return. Very large denomination notes are also made by the Bank of England and issued to the note issuing banks of Scotland and Northern Ireland, so that the notes they circulate are always supported by the same amount in Bank of England sterling currency.

Appendix I. Comparative Catalogue Numbers for Treasury Notes

A Comparison table of the reference numbers in this book, and the two other most popular references for English banknotes.

CBN = This book, "Collectors' Bank Notes".
Duggleby = "English Paper Money" by V. Duggleby (7th edition used).
Pick = The "Standard Catalog of World Paper Money", originally by Albert Pick (The 10th edition (Vol. 2) and 9th edition (Vol. 3) were referred to).

CBN	Duggleby	Pick	CBN	Duggleby	Pick
ONE SHILLING			**ONE POUND**		
RT1	T23	-	RT25a	T1	P347
RT2	T29	P353	RT25b	T1	P347
			RT25c	T1	P347
HALF CROWN			RT26a	T2	P347
			RT26b	-	P347
RT3	T22	-	RT26c	-	P347
RT4	T28	P354	RT27a	T3 Type 1	P347
			RT27b	T3 Type 2	P347
FIVE SHILLINGS			RT27c	T3 Type 3	P347
			RT27d	T3 Type 4	P347
RT5	T21	P352	RT28a	T4 Type 1	P347
RT6	T27	P355	RT28b	T4 Type 2	P347
			RT29a	T5 Type 3a	P347
TEN SHILLINGS			RT29b	T5 Type 4	P347
			RT29c	T5 Type 3b	
RT7	T8	P346	RT30	T6	P347
			RT31	T7	P347
RT8	T9	P346	RT32	T11 Type 1	P349a
RT8a	T9	P346	RT33	T11 Type 2	P349a
RT9	T10	P346	RT34	T14	P349b
RT10	T12 Type 1	P348a	RT35	T16	P351
RT11	T12 Type 2	P348a	RT36	T24	P357
RT12	T12 Type 3	P348a	RT36a	T24	P357
RT13	T13 Type 1	P348a	RT37	T31	P359a
RT14	T13 Type 2	P348a	RT38	T32	P359b
RT15	T15	P348b	RT39	T34	P361a
RT16	T17	P350a	RT40	T35	P361b
RT17	T18	P350a			
RT18	T19	P350b			
RT19	T20	P350b			
RT20	T25	P356			
RT21	T26	P356			
RT22	T30	P358			
RT23a	T33	P360			
RT23b	T33a	P360			

Appendix II. Comparative Catalogue Numbers for Bank of England Notes

CBN	Duggleby	Pick
HALF CROWN		
RB1	B254	P364
FIVE SHILLINGS		
RB2	B253	P365
TEN SHILLINGS		
RB3	B210	P362a
RBS3	B210s	-
RB5	B223	P362b
RBS5	B223s	-
RB7	B235	P362c
RBS7	B235s	-
RB8	B236	P362c
RB10	B251	P366
RBS10	B251s	-
RB12	B256	P362c
RBS12	B256s	-
RB14	B262	P368a
RB15	B263	P368a
RB16	B265	P368b
RB17	B266	P368b
RB18	B267	P368b
RB19	B271	P368c
RBS19	B271s	-
RB20	B272	P368c
RB21	B286	P373a
RBS21	B286s	-
RB22	B287	P373a
RB23	B294	P373b
RBS23	B294s	-
RB24	B295	P373b
RB25	B296	P373b
RB26	B309	P373c
RBS26	B309s	-
RB27	B310	P373c
RB28	B311	P373c
ONE POUND		
RB31	B212	P363a
RBS31	B212s	-
RB33	B225	P363b
RBS33	B225s	-
RB34	B226	P363b
RB36	B238	P363c
RB37	B239	P363c
RB41	B248	P367a
ONE POUND (GUERNSEY O/P)		
RBG31a	B212(A)	P363e
RBG33a	B225(A)	P363f

CBN	Duggleby	Pick
ONE POUND (GUERNSEY O/P)		
RBG34a	B226(A)	P363f
RBG36a	B238(A)	P363g
RBG37a	B239(A)	P363h
RBG37b	B239(B)	P363i
RBG37c	B239(C)	P363j
RBG41a	B248(A)	P367b
RBG42a	B249(A)	P367c
ONE POUND		
RBS41	B?	
RB42	B249	P367a
RBS42	B249s	-
RB44	B258	P363d
RBS44	B258s	-
RB46	B260	P369a
RB47	B261	P369a
RB51	B268	P369b
RBS51	B268s	-
RB52	B269	P369b
RB53	B273	P369c
RBS53	B273s	-
RB54	B274	P369c
RB61	B281	P374a
RBS61	B281s	-
RB62	B282	P374a
RB63	B283	P374b
RB64	B284	P374a
RB65	B285	P374a
RB66	B288	P374c
RB67	B289	P374c
RB68	B290	P374c
RB69	B291	P374c
RB70	B292	P374d
RB71	B293	P374d
RB72	B301	P374e
RB73	B302	P374e
RB74	B303	P374f
RB75	B304	P374f
RB76	B305	P374e
RB77	B306	P374e
RB78	B307	P374f
RB79	B308	P374f
RB81a	B320	P374g
RB81b	B320	P374g
RB82	B321	P374g
RB83	B322	P374g
RB84	B323	P374g
RB85	B337	P377a
RB86	B338	P377a
RB87	B339	P377a
RB87E	B339a	-
RB88	B340	P377a
RB89	B341	P377b
RB90	B342	P377b

The International Bank Note Society (IBNS) was formed in 1961 as a non-profit organization. The IBNS is organized for educational purposes and in furtherance of such purpose, its objectives are to promote, stimulate and advance the study and knowledge of world wide banknotes and paper currencies. Currently the IBNS has more than 2,000 members in over 90 countries.

Members can enjoy a number of benefits, for example: a quality journal and newsletter containing information on new issues, learned studies on paper money, and a worthwhile list of contacts and dealers to further their collections and studies.

To join the International Bank Note Society please make a photocopy of this page (or write a letter with the required details as outlined below) and send it to the society's General Secretary Clive Rice who will also be pleased to answer any questions you may wish to ask. His contact details are shown below. This form is also available for download in the Collectors Banknote section on www.rotographic.co.uk

Name: (as you wish it to appear on your membership card)

Telephone Number: (Include country code if outside the UK)

Address:

Email address:

Type of membership required (fees payable annually):

- ☐ **Individual Membership** (£16.50 / US$33.00 / EUR25.00)
- ☐ **Junior Membership** (£8.25 / US$16.50 / EUR10.00)
- ☐ **Family Membership** (£20.50 / US$41.00 / EUR30.00)
- ☐ **Further details only please**

GB£ and US$ may be sent as a cheque or money order payable to I.B.N.S. The General Secretary is also able to accept most other currencies if prior contact is made. The website of the IBNS is www.theIBNS.org

Please Post to the General Secretary:

Mr Clive Rice,
25 Copse Side, Binscombe,
Godalming, Surrey, GU7 3RU, (ENGLAND)

The General Secretary can also be contaced via email: IBNSuk@onetel.com

Appendix II. Comparative Catalogue Numbers for Bank of England Notes (continued)

CBN	Duggleby	Pick	CBN	Duggleby	Pick
	FIVE POUNDS			**FIVE POUNDS**	
RB101	B215	P320	RB126	B344	P378c
RBS101	B215s	-	RB127	B345	P378d
RB102	B228	P328	RBS127	B345s	-
RBS102	B228s	-	RB128	B353	P378e
RB103	B241	P335	RB501	B357	P382a/b
RBS103	B241s	-	RB502	B362	P382c
RB104	B255	P342	RB503	B363	-
RBS104	B255s	-	RB504	B364	-
RB105	B264	P343	RB504b	B365	-
RBS105	B264s	-	RB505	C119	-
RB106	B270	P344	RB505b	C122a	-
RBS106	B270s	-	RB505c	C123	-
RB107	B275	P345	RB505d	C126	-
RBS107	B275s	-	RB506	C130	-
RB108	B276	P345	RB506b	C135	-
RB109	B277	P371	RB506c	C139	-
RBS109	B277s	-	RB507	B378	-
RB110	B280	P372	RB508	B379	-
RBS110	B280s	-	RB509	C149	-
RB111	B297	P375a	RB510	C152	-
RBS111	B297s	-	RB510b	C153	-
RB112	B298	P375a	RB511	B395	P392a/b
RB113	B312	P375b	RB511b	B397	-
RBS113	B312s	-	RB512	B396	P392a/b
RB114	B313	P375b	RB513	C160	-
RB115	B314	P375b	RB514	C164	-
RB116	B315	P375b	RB515	B398	-
RB117	B324	P375c			
RB118	B325	P375c		**TEN POUNDS**	
RB119	B332	P378a			
RBS119	B332s	-	RB151	B216	P321
RB120	B333	P378a	RB152	B229	P329
RB121	B334	P378b	RB153	B242	P336
RBS121	B334s	-	RB154	B299	P376a
RB122	B335	P378b	RBS154	B299s	-
RB123	B336	P378b	RB156	B316	P376b
RB124	B343	P378c	RBS156	B316s	-
			RB158	B326	P376c
			RBS158	B326s	-
			RB159	B327	P376c
			RB161	B330	P379a
			RBS161	B330s	-
			RB162	B331	P379a
			RB163	B346	P379b
			RB164	B347	P379b
			RB165	B348	P379b
			RB166	B349	P379c
			RBS166	B349	-
			RB167	B354	P379d
			RB168	B360	P379e

Appendix II. Comparative Catalogue Numbers for Bank of England Notes (continued)

TEN POUNDS

CBN	Duggleby	Pick
RB1001	B366	P383
RB1002	B367	-
RB1003	B368	P386a
RB1003b	B369	P386a
RB1004	C120	CS3
RB1004b	C124	-
RB1004c	C127	-
RB1005	C131	-
RB1005b	C136	-
RB1006	B380	-
RB1006b	B381	-
RB1006c	C150	CS11
RB1006d	C154	-
RB1007	B388	P389a
RB1007b	B389	P389a
RB1008	B390	P389b
RB1009	B391	P389b
RB1010	C159	-
RB1010b	C161	-
RB1011	B400	P389c

TWENTY POUNDS

CBN	Duggleby	Pick
RB171	B217	P322
RB172	B230	P330
RB173	B243	P337
RB174	B318	P380a
RBS174	B318s	-
RB175	B319	P380a
RB176	B328	P380b
RB177	B329	P380b
RB178	B350	P380c
RBS178	B350s	-
RB180	B351	P380d
RBS180	B351s	-
RB181	B355	P380e
RB2000	B358	P384a
RB2000b	B359	P384a
RB2001	B358	-
RB2001b	B372/3	-
RB2002	B370	P384b
RB2003	B372	P387a
RB2003b	C128	-
RB2004	B373	P387a
RB2004b	B374	P387a
RB2005	B382	P387b
RB2006	-	-
RB2006b	B387	P390a

TWENTY POUNDS

CBN	Duggleby	Pick
RB2007	C151	-
RB2008	C155	-
RB2009	-	-
RB2010	C164	-
RB2011	-	-
RB2012	B402	P390b

FIFTY POUNDS

CBN	Duggleby	Pick
RB191	B218	P323
RB192	B231	P331
RB193	B244	P338
RB194	B352	P381a
RBS194	B352s	-
RB195	B356	P381b
RB196	B361	P381c
RB5001	B375	P388a
RB5001b	B377	-
RB5002	-	-
RB5002b	B378	-
RB5003	C132	-
RB5004	B383	P388b
RB5005	B404	-

ONE HUNDRED POUNDS

CBN	Duggleby	Pick
RB201	B219	P324
RB202	B232	P332
RB203	B245	P339

TWO HUNDRED POUNDS

CBN	Duggleby	Pick
RB220	B220	P325

FIVE HUNDRED POUNDS

CBN	Duggleby	Pick
RB221	B221	P326
RB222	B233	P333
RB223	B246	P340

ONE THOUSAND POUNDS

CBN	Duggleby	Pick
RB301	B222	P327
RB302	B234	P334
RB303	B247	P341

Bibliography - Suggested further reading

As Good As Gold - V Hewitt/J Keyworth, British Museum Publications.

Bank of England and Treasury Notes - D M Miller, Corbitt & Hunter.

Discovering Banknotes - K R Lake, Shire Publications.
ISBN 0852631650

English Paper Money - V Duggleby, Pam West (Publisher).
ISBN 0954345711

Nazi Counterfeiting of British Currency During WWII - B O Burke,
Book Shop (Publisher).   ISBN 0961827408

Promises to Pay - D Byatt/Bank of England, Spink and Son.
ISBN 0907605508

The Money Makers - W Kranister, Blackbear Publishing.

The Story of Money - Whitehead/Baskerville, Usborne Publishing.

The Story of Paper Money - Y Beresiner/C Narbeth,
David & Charles Ltd.   ISBN 0715357530

Standard Catalog of World Paper Money Vol 2, 10th Edition -
A Pick/Various editors.   ISBN 087349704X

Standard Catalog of World Paper Money Vol 3, 9th Edition -
A Pick/Various editors.   ISBN 0873495918

Some Useful websites of Bank note Dealers etc

www.britishnotes.co.uk
www.thebanknotestore.com
www.collectpapermoney.co.uk
www.theIBNS.org (The International Bank Note Society)
www.ibnslondon.org.uk (The IBNS in London)
www.banknotes4u.co.uk
www.colin-narbeth.com
www.worldnotes.co.uk
www.katespapermoney.com

Coincraft

WE WANT YOUR NOTES!

Coincraft desperately needs banknotes and is willing to pay spec[ial] prices for British and world notes. Maybe you should think abo[ut] selling your notes; it could be well worth y[our] while!

White notes, Bank of England notes, Treasu[ry] notes, Provincial notes; if you have them, w[e] want them! With over 4,000 banknote buyer[s] our mailing list we are always in need of m[ore] notes. Perhaps you can help us and make you[r] self some money at the same time!

English notes, Scottish notes and Irish notes ar[e] especially in demand at this moment and that i[s] reflected in our excellent prices. Single notes, [origi]nal blocks of notes, hoards or collections; we a[re] happy to buy notes in any quantity. We also want world notes; either as sing[le] important notes, whole collections or accumu[la]tions.

We paid over £240,000 when we bought the famous lot of British military notes at auction[. If] you want to sell your notes without any hassle[, at] an excellent price and for immediate on the sp[ot] payment, then please contact Claire Lobel.

Call in person at either of our two shops at 44 & 45 Great Russell Street, just across from the British Museum. Open Monday to Friday 9.30 to 5.00 and Saturday from 10.00 till 2.30.

Friendly, personal service and an interesting display of coins, banknotes, medallions, ancient coins and antiquities, to tempt and delight you.

Buy by post through Britain's only coin newspaper, The Phoenix, published every three weeks. It contains 24 tabloid sized pages of special offers and rare items, many not available anywhere else.

You can't buy a subscription, but you can get a complimentary copy free, just for the asking.

On the Internet Our website, www.coincraft.com is available 24 hours a day. There are many interesting features including a comprehensive numismatic glossary. Keep looking, more is being added every day.

Coincra[ft]
FRIENDLY PROFESSIONAL SERVICE SIN[CE]

We always need to buy Coincraft needs to buy: single items to entire collections, dealers inventories, hoards, accumulations, you name it and we will make you an offer. Over 90% of our offers are accepted. Sell where the dealers sell.

Tel 020 7636 1188 and 020 763[.] Fax 020 7323 2860 and 020 763[.]

Find out why collectors say; Coincraft, nice people to do business with.

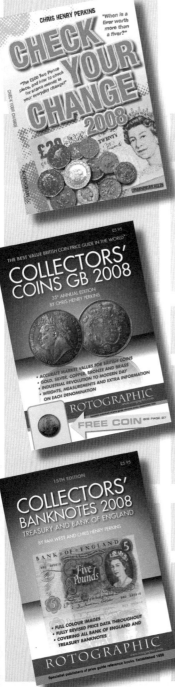